The National Railway Museum

INTRODUCTION
by **John A. Coiley,** *Keeper*

The National Railway Museum operates as part of the Science Museum, in the Department of Education and Science. By the summer of 1982 the Museum will have received ten million visitors since the opening on 27 September 1975.

The date and occasion were most appropriate. The first public railway to use a steam locomotive to haul passengers opened 150 years earlier between Stockton and Darlington. The first railway museum in Britain was opened by the former London & North Eastern Railway in York in 1928. That museum had been prompted by the need to house a number of relics assembled three years earlier for the Centenary celebrations of the Stockton & Darlington Railway.

The National Railway Museum results directly from the 1968 Transport Act when it was decided that the British Railway Board should pass responsibility for its railway historical relics, which by then included many in the larger British Transport Museum at Clapham in South London, to the Department of Education and Science which in this context meant the Science Museum. Furthermore, the British Railways Board would find and provide, in consultation with the Science Museum, a suitable site and building for the new museum. It was subsequently decided to refurbish and extend part of the old York North Motive Power Depot, for the rehousing of the railway exhibits from the York Queen Street and Clapham Museums, and work began early in 1973.

By skilful design the British Railways architects have retained much of the atmosphere of the old steam engine shed in the new Museum, while conveying a light and spacious feeling to the Main Exhibition Hall. The associated new building is an efficient and compact housing for a wide range of ancillary services for the Museum including the library, workshops, lecture theatre, photographic studio, shop and refreshment room. An important feature of the new site is the direct rail connection with the British Rail system. This allows relatively easy interchange of rolling stock by rail, a valuable consideration when the reserve collection includes heavy engineering items such as locomotives and carriages.

THE MAIN HALL
The entrance of the Museum leads directly to the Main Exhibition Hall which covers two acres. Here the locomotives and rolling stock are displayed around the two original turntables. Other major items are exhibited against the walls of the building together with many showcases whose contents complement the collection of large exhibits, and the selected free-standing items throughout the Hall. Overlooking all these exhibits is a specially constructed wide viewing balcony.

Ground Floor
The major display of technical material is located on the Ground Floor of the Main Hall. On entering visitors immediately see two of the major exhibits of the Museum. Firstly, a completely new addition to the collection, a fully sectioned rebuilt 'Pacific' locomotive *Ellerman Lines*, which may be friction driven by an electric motor to show the working of the valve gear. Secondly, the Weatherhill stationary winding engine, an important and long-lived link in the change from the use of horses to the almost universal adoption of steam locomotives. Another notable item in the entrance area is the famous statue of George Stephenson from the former Great Hall at Euston Station. Taken together, these three exhibits perhaps help to set the pattern for the rest of the Museum: the intention to cover all the aspects of railway operation and the importance of people, whether they were famous railway engineers or the public served by the railways.

Moving forward into the Hall, the motive power collection may be studied, grouped around the larger electrically operated 70-ft turntable. Although the locomotives on display at any one time vary according to demands of restoration, preparation for working trains, etc., there will always be a wide range of steam locomotives to be seen together with notable examples of electric and diesel traction, including components such as power units and transmission systems. The

1. *Driving wheel of Ivatt 'Atlantic' No. 251.*

locomotives on view range from *The Agenoria* of 1829 (the year *Rocket* appeared) and lent to the old York Railway Museum by the Science Museum many years ago, the record-breaking *Mallard* of 1938 with its proud achievement for steam of 126 m.p.h. (203 km/h.), and *Evening Star*, the last steam locomotive built by British Railways in March 1960 at Swindon, to more modern types such as the 'Deltic' class diesel electric (only withdrawn from service at the end of 1981) and the experimental version of the Advanced Passenger Train (APT-E), the prototype of which started revenue earning trials in 1981. In addition to these splendid machines are examples of some of the most famous locomotives of all time, such as the Stirling 'Single' of 1870, the North Eastern Railway engine of the 1895 'Races to the North' 4–4–0 No. 1621, the very efficient Adams 4–4–0 No. 563, and perhaps the most elegant locomotive ever built, the Wainwright 4–4–0 of 1901 which with its magnificent livery is so typical of the age it represents.

The wall cases surrounding this turntable display locomotive technical details (such as injectors, regulators, whistles, safety valves, valve gear models) together with a wide range of locomotive models, many with working features. In the future, special models will be commissioned to fill gaps in the sequence of the prototype collection which can now never be filled with original material.

The other end of this Hall houses the rolling stock collection centred around a 60-ft decked turntable. At present this display comprises largely passenger vehicles (many very specialised) but it is hoped in due course to redress this balance and to show more typical vehicles including classic examples of electric multiple unit stock as well as more recent examples of Royal coaches, and to reflect the importance of the freight vehicle in British railway history. Some of the latter may now usually be seen outside the Main Hall (near the car park area) and will be interchanged with others as the restoration programme proceeds. Some of the oldest and most interesting examples are, however, to be found inside and include the Peak Forest Canal truck of 1797, an early coal (chaldron) wagon and a replica of a 'dandy-cart'.

Among the carriage collection the Royal coaches take pride of place even if they are not representative of public travel of the time. They range from Queen Adelaide's coach of 1842, still clearly related to the stage coach, through the sumptuous saloons built in the Edwardian era to more modern vehicles of 1941 which were used by the present Royal Family until 1977. Despite its age, having been built originally in 1869 as two separate (day and night) saloons, Queen Victoria's Saloon is still a major attraction amid this splendid collection. The interior furnishings are original and now present a formidable task in conservation. In 1981/1982 all the Royal Saloons at York were displayed in the 'Palaces on Wheels' exhibition to celebrate the wedding of H.R.H. the Prince and Princess of Wales. It is hoped that on some future occasions it will be possible to display again this rich collection in its entirety.

Ordinary passenger vehicles range from the Bodmin & Wadebridge carriages, parts dating from the early 1830s, to the British Railways Mk I open saloon of the mid-1950s refurbished by the National Railway Museum for use as a children's study coach. In between there are a number of fascinating carriages. They include a finely restored Midland Railways six-wheel composite carriage of 1885, an example of the carriages which set the pattern for railway passengers' travel when the Midland Railway abolished the second-class and upgraded third-class accommodation. Other notable more recent additions include a 1925 Southern Railway electric motor coach and a 1936 Wagons Lits car from the 'Night Ferry' service, between London and Paris and Brussels.

The motive power and rolling-stock collections have always dominated the Museum displays due to their size. Their success and operation, however, has always depended upon a strong, reliable and well-maintained track (the 'permanent way') and an effective, reliable and fail-safe signalling system. In the present layout of the Museum there is still only room for an outline of the salient points in the history of these areas. It is intended, however, that in due course a more comprehensive display will be made available to do justice to the importance of these subjects and to the extensive and valuable reserve collection built up over the years and still growing.

Nevertheless, there is already much for the visitor to see. A wide range of rail samples are shown from early plate-way material to early iron bull-head and modern steel flat-bottomed rail. There are also examples of the different methods used to secure rails to sleepers and the various kinds of material used for the latter. The signal collection covers the change from the early 'time interval' method for keeping trains apart, through the start of the modern space ('block') interval methods with the arrival of telegraphy, the refinement of signal and track interlocking (with a prototype working display) to modern sophisticated automatic high-intensity colour light equipment based on centralised electronic control systems. It is hoped that future developments in this area will include an operational model layout.

Another important area of railway engineering which requires much more consideration in the future is that of civil engineering. A number of bridge models are included and the world's first iron railway bridge (on the Stockton to Darlington Railway over the River Gaunless near West Auckland, Co. Durham) has been

2. *Widening of Lime Street Tunnels, Liverpool, in 1885 – one of the historical photographic prints in the collection.*

re-erected outside the Museum near the main entrance. Again it is hoped in due course to provide a more detailed treatment of this subject, including the problems and techniques, maintenance as well as modern developments.

The display on the Ground Floor is completed by a miscellaneous selection of free-standing items such as clocks, ticket machines, etc., and the extensive wall display of train headboards, locomotive nameplates, station nameboards and railway notices.

Special Exhibitions Gallery

This is a self-contained gallery entered from the Main Hall and so far has been used to accommodate special exhibitions usually associated with an important anniversary of some kind. Topics covered have included Centenary of the Settle–Carlisle Line, Royal Trains, Station Hotels and Electric Traction 1879–1979.

It is now being used for a more permenant display likely to last 4-5 years covering all aspects of Model Railways. The basis for this exhibition consists of two working model railways. One, kindly lent by the builders, the Scalefour Society, is a 4 mm fine scale model which is arranged to demonstrate train operation at a typical country station in the 1930s. The other model, built by the Museum to 7 mm fine scale, will display typical complete trains of the past 100 years. In a number of cases this will be an opportunity for trains from the smaller companies to be seen some bearing less familiar liveries. At the same time important and well known trains will feature, although in most cases with motive power and rolling stock the prototypes for which no longer exist. Complementing these railways will be displays of model railways from classic toy models including early tin plate examples to present day larger scale live steam model engineering exercises.

To a great extent the working model railways are experimental. Changes will be incorporated in the light of experience of extended operation and the results of these operations will form the basis of future working layouts to be built when more space is available.

Balcony

The Main Hall may be viewed from the specially-built, wide, full-length balcony. Besides giving a further opportunity to study the motive power and rolling stock from a different viewpoint, the balcony provides a further display area for the absorbing story of the history of British railways. This treatment covers in sequence the development of railways in Britain as a whole, emphasising the economic and social impact of railways. It comprises a wide range of the smaller historical material to complement the larger exhibits on the Ground Floor, including manuscripts of the early railway engineers, their equipment, early railway company seals, contemporary models of locomotives and carriages (some as early toy trains), early locomotive and carriage equipment, timetables, maps, early trade union material, the railway export industry, modern railway activity and models of future equipment and buildings.

Further along the balcony there are displays devoted to 'railwayana', railway toys, china, silverware, buttons, promotional leaflets, etc., from the different pre-grouping companies. Another display

3. *One of the many railway posters in the collection.*

covers the extensive shipping interests of the railways by means of a selection of fine scale model ships. Other items include York as a railway centre, and the background to the railway ticket.

Since the Museum opened, a small audio-visual theatre has been established in the middle of this gallery. This theatre has been used to illustrate some of the more varied aspects of railway operations by means of colour slides and commentaries especially prepared by Museum staff.

FRONT GALLERY

This gallery is a spur from the upper entrance hall and includes a selection of material ranging from stained-glass station windows, contemporary models, early uniforms modelled by wax figures, restaurant car and hotel silver, glass and chinaware, paintings and photographs, all exemplifying the use made by the railways of art and design during their day-to-day business and in their promotion of that business.

4. *The nameplate of* Rocket.

LECTURE THEATRE AND EDUCATIONAL SERVICES
The Museum possesses a comprehensively equipped lecture theatre/cinema seating up to eighty. A ramped floor is provided, allowing a good view of the special demonstration bench where working models are explained during lectures on scientific and engineering subjects which provide background to past and present railway operations. Although primarily intended for school parties and students, the lecture theatre and educational facilities are available to all. Details of these services are contained in a leaflet available free by writing to the Education Officer.

LIBRARY
The Museum collection of books, records, mechanical engineering drawings, negatives and photographs is administered by the Librarian and his staff. While the library is intended primarily as a source of information for research work and for the Museum

5. *Midland Railway armorial bearings.*

staff, the library staff are always pleased to try to answer written enquiries, although the time that they can devote to such work is strictly limited.

The library collection is only available for consultation on Tuesday to Friday by *prior application in writing* to the Librarian for a Reader's Ticket.

In due course, some of the more notable material in the collection will become available by direct publication or by incorporation in books. For the full range of NRM publications, visitors should enquire at the Museum Shop.

THE FUTURE
Since opening, the Museum collections have grown, visitor amenities have improved, particularly the shop and refreshment room, and valuable storage space has been acquired. These developments in one way or another have enabled the Museum to present a more comprehensive and better balanced exhibition. Much more work of this kind is, however, necessary to achieve our objective to illustrate the story of railways in the United Kingdom, from the time of Industrial Revolution until the present day, and to look at probable future development. That is to say, the presentation of a continuous railway story.

In particular, while it was natural for British Railways' collection, which we inherited, to concentrate on their own history, a large railway industry grew up in this country independently of the major main-line railway companies. More of the story of this industry is being incorporated in the Museum's display including notable examples from home and overseas markets, such as a 1935 Vulcan built 4–8–4 locomotive from China.

In common with all museums covering the field of transport, the presentation of movement, which is so essential to the story, is a major problem. Although working exhibits, models, films, etc., go some way to overcoming the inevitable static feeling of the Museum, it is only by actually operating some of our locomotives and carriages that the spirit of railways can be captured. By mutual co-operation with British Railways Board and various preservation groups, the National Railway Museum is sometimes able to operate some of its historic locomotives and rolling stock. Our resources for this kind of activity, which can only be undertaken with great regard to security of the unique material involved, are nevertheless limited. We have however been pleased with the attention attracted by the working reproduction 'Rocket' built in 1979 to celebrate the 150th anniversary of this famous locomotive. Such projects and the operation of purpose-built live steam models of the Museum together with increased use of modern video and film techniques, point the way ahead for our efforts to create a 'live' museum.

Although our growing collection of restored material, both large and small, enables variations to the public exhibition, there are a number of major improvements we wish to make as soon as circumstances allow. It is hoped that it will be possible in due course to open to visitors much of the storage space acquired in recent years. In this way it should be possible, not only to display, much more of the present collection, but use it to tell a more integrated story, to try to convey the experience of travel by train in the past and to say much more about the railway of today and the future.

6. *The sectioned locomotive in detail.*

Locomotives

DESCRIPTION OF PRINCIPAL EXHIBITS
by **Peter W. B. Semmens,** *The Assistant Keeper*

On the following pages there are brief descriptions of the principal exhibits at the National Railway Museum. Like most museums, there are more exhibits than can be displayed simultaneously, and it is therefore our policy to change the rolling stock on exhibition. Visitors will thus never find all the vehicles that are described on show together, but it is hoped that this text will provide an indication of the importance of each exhibit. In the case of those that are on display, there will normally be a label board alongside which gives a more extensive description together with the more important dimensions, weights and other appropriate data.

The Main Hall of the new Museum was once the repair section of York North Motive Power Depot, which serviced the large number of steam locomotives allocated to handle the traffic from this very important railway centre. The layout is based on two turntables. The more northern of these, the 'A' turntable, has

been retained in its original condition and is used predominantly to display the locomotives spread out around the 24 tracks that radiate from it. One track has been completely rebuilt with a new deep pit, through which visitors can walk to see the underside of the locomotive on it. Another track crosses over to the 'B' turntable which has the coaches and wagons arranged on most of its 20 tracks. In this case, however, the turntable pit has been decked in to facilitate the circulation of visitors around the exhibition. The 'A' turntable retains its electrical operation, but the 'B' turntable is moved by means of a fork-lift truck or the Museum's 'Locopulsor' – a small, manually-operated machine with a 5 h.p. motor which is capable of moving the various items of rolling stock. Two tracks from the 'A' turntable lead out across the car park area to connect with British Railways' lines. These enable exhibits to be exchanged with those in the reserve collection and allow operational vehicles to move in and out.

Locomotives

Shutt End Colliery 0–4–0 'Agenoria' (1829)
This locomotive was a contemporary of the Stephensons' *Rocket* which won the Rainhill Trials, but represents a much earlier design concept, being one of the many attempts to produce a mobile beam engine. It is the oldest locomotive in the Museum, and was acquired by the Science Museum in 1884. The locomotive is almost identical with the *Stourbridge Lion*, also built in 1829 and exported to America where it was the first locomotive to run on rails in that continent.

Replica of Liverpool & Manchester Railway 0–2–2 'Rocket' (1829/1979)
The Stephensons' *Rocket*, which won the Rainhill Trials in 1829, is probably the most well-known steam locomotive in the world. To mark the 150th Anniversary of the original's construction, the Museum commissioned Locomotion Enterprises of Springwell, Tyne & Wear, to construct a working replica, which first ran in public in Kensington Gardens in August 1979. The locomotive has appeared at numerous sites in England as well as abroad. It has visited France, Holland, and Australia, in addition to California, when it became the first steam locomotive to *fly* the Atlantic.

Grand Junction Railway 2–2–2 No. 1868, 'Columbine' (1845)
This locomotive was the first example of the standard 'Crewe'-type engine with 6 ft diameter driving wheels. Many of the early locomotives had inside cylinders, driving on to a crank axle, which was a source of weakness. Buddicom and Francis Trevithick (son of the famous Richard) accordingly developed this sturdy outside-cylinder design which influenced British locomotive thinking for more than forty years. The locomotive was originally preserved in the form in which it was withdrawn in 1902, but has now had its cab removed so that it appears as it did in the early 1870s.

Furness Railway 0–4–0 No. 3 'Coppernob' (1846)
Edward Bury was one of the rivals of the Stephensons as an early locomotive engineer, and his designs differed in a number of marked respects from those of his contemporaries. Not only did he use frames made of iron bars rather than flat plates, but his fireboxes had a characteristic shape. They were D-shaped in plan, and had a hemispherical top, clad in copper sheet, which gave the locomotive its nickname of 'Coppernob'. This locomotive remained at work until 1900, and was then exhibited outside the station at Barrow-in-Furness. The holes made by the bomb splinters during the Second World War air raid are still visible.

North Eastern Railway 2–2–4 tank No. 66, 'Aerolite' (1869–1902)
This delightful little tank engine is the last of the standard-gauge two-cylinder compounds to survive in this country. It was built in 1869 as a 2–2–2 well-tank, and successive rebuildings took place in 1886, 1892 and 1902. It became, for a period, a 4–2–2 tank before assuming its present wheel arrangement. It was in its present form that it lasted longest, being used to haul the departmental saloons around the NER and LNER North-Eastern Area until it was withdrawn in 1933.

It was repainted at the Doncaster Works of British Rail Engineering Ltd in 1980.

Great Northern Railway 4–2–2 No. 1 (1870)
The Stirling Singles of the GNR were notable for their elegant appearance, typical of the locomotive designs adopted in the last decades of the nineteenth century for main-line express passenger trains. No. 1 was the first of this class to be built, and was shedded at Doncaster throughout its thirty-seven-year life, being withdrawn in 1907. It was subsequently steamed for publicity purposes in 1938. In 1981 it was again restored to steaming condition at the NRM, and has operated trains on the Great Central Railway at Loughborough.

Stockton & Darlington Railway 0–6–0 No. 1275 (1874)
The Stockton & Darlington Railway continued the use of the Stephensons' long-boiler design, and this locomotive, a development of the 'Hippopotamus' class, was actually built after it had been absorbed by the North Eastern Railway in 1863. It was constructed by Dübs & Co. of Glasgow and remained in service until 1923, when it was set aside for preservation. It was on display at Darlington North Road Station Museum from 1975 until 1982.

North Eastern Railway 2–4–0 No. 910 (1875)
The 2–4–0 wheel arrangement was popular with locomotive engineers in the latter half of the last century, but Edward Fletcher's design, built over a ten-year period, was a good deal heavier than many contemporary types. The appearance of the locomotive was carefully considered too, as the elaborate polished fittings and livery show. In its preserved form it is fitted with the non-automatic version of the vacuum brake, with the two ejectors on the side of the smokebox. This particular locomotive is noteworthy, as it took part in the 50th, 100th and 150th anniversary celebrations of the opening of the Stockton & Darlington Railway.

London, Brighton & South Coast Railway Class 'A' 0–6–0 tank No. 82, 'Boxhill' (1880)
Between 1872 and 1880, William Stroudley produced fifty small tank engines to work the suburban services in South and East London. In spite of their small size they worked very hard and

7. *The Stirling Single in operation on the Great Central Railway in 1981.* (Photo: L. A. Nixon)

were soon nicknamed 'Rooters' or 'Terriers', the latter term becoming almost an official reference in their later years. Their low weight subsequently enabled them to work on some lightly-constructed branch lines, and several lasted well into British Railways' days. *Boxhill* was restored at Brighton Works in 1947. A similar engine, *Waddon*, is exhibited in the Canadian Railroad Museum at Montreal, while another eight have also been preserved in various places but not in their original condition. This particular member of the class is fitted with equipment for condensing the exhaust steam in the water contained in the side tanks.

London, Brighton & South Coast Railway 0–4–2 No. 214 'Gladstone' (1882)

The 0–4–2 wheel arrangement is an unusual one for an express passenger locomotive, having no guiding wheels in front of the leading drivers. *Gladstone* was the first locomotive to be preserved by a society as distinct from a railway company. In 1927 it was obtained from the Southern Railway by the Stephenson Locomotive Society, and put on display in the newly-opened York Railway Museum. *Gladstone* was presented to the British Transport Commission by the Society in 1959 to become part of the National Collection, and is now usually exhibited with the regalia carried by the LB & SCR's Royal Trains. It is painted in Stroudley's 'Improved Engine Green', the most probable explanation for which was that the designer was colour blind, although there is a school of thought which maintains that Stroudley's words were that it was: 'an improvement on engine green'.

Lancashire & Yorkshire Railway Narrow-Gauge Locomotive 'Wren' (1887)

This was one of a batch of engines built by Beyer-Peacock & Co., in 1887 for the 18 in.-gauge works tramway system at Horwich. There were eight of these locomotives, of which *Wren* was the last survivor. It has a boiler pressure of 180 lb per sq. in. (12·4 bar) and weighs in working order 3 tons 11 cwt 2 qr (3·6 tonnes). It worked until 1957, after which it was kept until 1963

as a standby for the diesel locomotive which replaced it. Heavy loads were handled by these locomotives from one part of the works to another. One of their lighter duties was to distribute wages round the workshops.

London & North Western Railway 'Precedent' Class 2–4–0 No. 790, 'Hardwicke' (1892)

Like the North Eastern 4–4–0 No. 1621, this locomotive was a participant in the Race to Aberdeen' in August 1895. Then it ran the 141 miles from Crewe to Carlisle at a start-to-stop average of 67·2 m.p.h. on one section of the record of 512 minutes for the 540 miles from Euston to Aberdeen. The locomotive is nominally a rebuild of an 1872 engine, but in fact was virtually completely new, being constructed to an 1874 design. The locomotive was restored to working order at Steamtown Railway Museum, Carnforth, in 1975, since when it has frequently been in operation on special trains of one sort or another, or for filming purposes.

Lancashire & Yorkshire Railway 2–4–2 tank No. 1008 (1889)

This was the first of 330 similar locomotives that were built over the period 1889–1911, and which were, by the end of that time, working more than half of that railway's passenger mileage. The symmetrical wheel arrangement permitted the engines to run at speed in either direction, and they were fitted with scoops to enable them to pick up water from troughs when running forwards or backwards. No. 1008 was the first locomotive to be built at Horwich Works. It was withdrawn by British Railways in 1954 and after restoration was on exhibition at Tyseley before coming to York in 1976. It was repainted in 1977 and is substantially in its condition as first built.

London & South Western Railway Adams 4–4–0 No. 563 (1893)

This was one of sixty locomotives designed by William Adams (his final express engines for the LSWR) and built at Nine Elms in 1893. It was in service on the LSWR and SR from 1893 to 1945. It had actually been condemned in 1939, but was reinstated because of the outbreak of the Second World War. In 1948 it was restored to its original condition for the Waterloo Station centenary celebrations, and was later on display at Clapham. At York one of Adams's vortex blast-pipes is usually exhibited close to the locomotive. This was an early attempt to improve the draught through the fire and boiler, and its internal construction can be seen in one of the showcases. Access to this locomotive's footplate is usually possible, to give visitors an idea of the working space available for the crew of a steam locomotive.

North Eastern Railway Class 'M' 4–4–0 No. 1621 (1893)

Twenty of these fine engines were built by Wilson Worsdell for express passenger service on the North Eastern main lines. They were provided with spacious cabs, and by comparing the cab fittings with those on *Columbine*, it can be seen how much

more sophisticated they had become in the course of half a century. The locomotives' abilities were demonstrated during the 'Race to Aberdeen' during the summer of 1895. No. 1621 took part in the record East Coast run on the night of 21/22 August, when she came on the train at York, averaging 61·5 m.p.h. on the stretch to Newcastle. A sister engine then covered the longer distance to Edinburgh at the even higher average of 66 m.p.h. No. 1621 was repainted in 1975, by British Rail Engineering Ltd, at its Carriage Works in York.

Great Eastern Railway 2–4–0 'Intermediate' No. 490 (1895)
The Great Eastern Railway built this class of new locomotives for its secondary services, rather than use obsolescent main-line designs. A hundred of them were built between 1891 and 1902, and operated over the whole of their system. After Grouping in 1923, some of them moved further afield, and they were even employed on the line between Darlington and Penrith that crossed the Pennines at Stainmore Summit, 1,370 ft (418 m) above sea level. After withdrawal at the end of 1959, No. 490 was restored at Stratford Works as nearly as possible to its 1895 condition.

London & South Western Railway Class M7 0–4–4T No. 245 (1897)
The use of the 0–4–4 wheel arrangement for tank engines was quite common in late Victorian times. When Dugald Drummond moved from Scotland to England to become Chief Mechanical Engineer of the LSWR, he built 105 engines of this class for suburban passenger services. In Southern Railway days they became a common sight on branch lines all over the system, some of them being fitted with controls for push-pull operation. They are large engines, and were capable of achieving good speeds with light trains. No. 245 was in store at Preston Park, Brighton, for many years before coming to York, and has been repainted by British Rail Engineering Ltd at Derby Carriage Works.

Midland Railway 4–2–2 No. 673 (1897)
In the late Victorian era, the Midland Railway was noted for its extremely handsome single-driver express locomotives, nicknamed 'Spinners'. This was a period when the single-wheeler made a come-back on express trains as a result of the invention of steam sanding gear which gave the wheels sufficient grip to enable them to deal with the still relatively-light passenger trains of four- and six-wheel carriages. No. 673 is one of a class of ninety-six locomotives built between 1887 and 1900. It originally carried the number 118 and was withdrawn in 1928 for preservation. After exhibition at Leicester, it was restored to full working order by the Midland Railway Trust, and appeared in steam at the 'Rocket 150' celebrations. It is in its pre-First World War condition.

Waterloo & City Railway Electric Locomotive (1898)
The underground Waterloo & City Railway, 1 mile 46 chains (2 km) long, was opened from Waterloo to the Bank in 1898. It

operated with third-rail electrification, and was completely separate from the main-line system at a higher level, stock being transferred by a lift. This locomotive, built by Siemens Brothers of London (Works No. 6), was used for shunting the stock and also hauling coal wagons for the power station that provided the electricity supply. Werner von Siemens had pioneered the first practical form of electric rail traction at an exhibition in Berlin in 1879, and the locomotive was repainted in its Southern Railway livery for the Museum's exhibition to mark the centenary in 1979.

Great Northern Railway 'Atlantic' 4–4–2s Nos. 990, 'Henry Oakley' (1898) and 251 (1902)
Ivatt's two 'Atlantic' locomotives in the National Collection mark an important stage in the development of the express passenger steam locomotive. When *Henry Oakley* was built at Doncaster in 1898, it was the first British tender engine of this wheel arrangement. The 'Atlantic', however, was a fairly logical development of the Stirling 'Single', which also had outside cylinders. Four years after No. 990 had been built, Ivatt increased the potential of the basic design by putting a far larger boiler on the same frames, with a wide firebox set above the trailing wheels. Ninety-one of the later type were built, compared with twenty-one of the earlier ones. In the 1930s, after being fitted with high-temperature superheaters, the large 'Atlantics' regularly worked some of the fastest East Coast trains. Both locomotives hauled specials during 1953, and *Henry Oakley* was steamed several times during the period 1975–8.

Great Northern Railway 0–6–0ST No. 1247 (1899)
This is one of the large fleet of 0–6–0 saddle tank locomotives built for shunting and local freight workings on the Great Northern Railway. No. 1247 was constructed by Sharp Stewart & Co. of Glasgow, and when withdrawn from BR service in 1959 was purchased by Captain W. G. Smith, the first example of a locomotive being taken over in running order for preservation by an individual. It has worked on British Railways and on a number of preserved railways since, and in 1980 became the first main-line locomotive to be donated privately to the National Collection in full working order.

South Eastern & Chatham Railway
This locomotive was built at Ashford Works under the direction of H. S. Wainwright and the class was one of the most handsome in form and colour ever seen. The elaborate livery was designed by Wainwright himself and it will be noted that even the axleboxes on the tender are decorated. These locomotives worked the express passenger traffic from London to Dover, Folkestone and Margate for many years. When No. 737 was withdrawn from service (at Guildford, in October 1956), it was restored at Ashford Works and exhibited at Clapham.

Midland Railway 4–4–0 Compound No. 1000 (1902)
The use of compound locomotives in the UK was never as widespread as it was in some other countries, notably France. In 1902, however, S. W. Johnson on the Midland Railway introduced this locomotive, the first of a class of Smith System compounds that was to be built in successive batches for the next thirty years. The first forty-five were constructed by the Midland Railway, and a further 195 by the London Midland & Scottish Railway after the 1923 Grouping. The locomotive is exhibited in the form in which it was rebuilt in 1914. No. 1000 operated in normal traffic until 1951, but in 1959 was restored to its 1907 Midland Railway livery for working special trains before being put on exhibition in the Clapham Museum. It has been in steam on several occasions since its move to York.

Great Eastern Railway 0–6–0 tank No. 87 (1904)
The Great Eastern Railway operated one of the most intensive suburban services in the world from Liverpool Street Station, London. Steam locomotives were used, and were specially designed to give high rates of acceleration away from the frequent stops. No. 87 represents one of the last of the 0–6–0s built for this service. After being displaced by larger locomotives in the 1920s, these engines were relegated to shunting

9. *Waterloo & City Railway electric locomotive of 1898.*

duties, No. 87 remaining in service until 1960. The locomotive was capable of condensing its exhaust steam in the water in the side tanks while operating in tunnels, and also has a variable-orifice blast-pipe, the operation of which is shown in one of the showcases.

North Eastern Railway Bo-Bo Electric Locomotive No. 1 (1904)

Steam locomotives faced rival forms of motive power more than seventy years ago. At the turn of the century, North-East England pioneered many of the electrical supply systems, notable among the exponents being Charles Merz (1874–1940). Under his guidance, when the North Tyneside suburban lines were electrified in 1904, the short but steep connection from the main line at Manors down to the quayside was similarly altered. The locomotives operated for more than sixty years, well into British Railways' days. After being exhibited at Leicester, No. 1 was moved to York and in 1977 was restored to full NER livery. Some of the interior partitions in the cab have been removed to enable visitors to see the banks of starting resistors.

Great Western Railway 2–8–0 No. 2818 (1905)

This class of locomotive was introduced in 1903 and set the pattern for heavy British freight locomotives for the next fifty years. Churchward copied many American design features, and the result was a very successful locomotive, and even as late as 1948 the class proved to be the most economical of all the freight designs tested by British Railways. The locomotive exhibits many of the classical Great Western Railway features, but being a freight engine it has not got a copper-capped chimney, and it is not lined out. No. 2818 has come to the National Railway Museum from the City of Bristol Museums, at whose cost it was restored by British Rail Engineering Ltd, at their Eastleigh works.

Beyer-Peacock 2 ft-gauge Garratt 0–4–0+0–4–0 Locomotive (1909)

This was the first Garratt locomotive, with separate engine units at each end supporting the boiler unit. The flexibility of this arrangement enabled far larger locomotives to be built than would otherwise have been the case, especially for lines that had severe curvature. This particular design is a compound, with cylinders at the inner ends of the power bogies. Virtually all the subsequent Garratts were simple-expansion machines and the cylinders were mounted at the outer ends.

This locomotive was built for the NE Dundas Tramway in Tasmania, and was brought back to England for preservation by Beyer-Peacock in 1947. With the closure of their works at Manchester in 1966, the locomotive was sold to the Festiniog Railway in North Wales, who have loaned it to the Museum. It has been repainted in 'works grey', indicative of the type of livery often adopted when locomotives were sent overseas from the private building firms. It is on a short length of Festiniog Railway 1 ft 11⅝ in.-gauge (60 cm) track, mounted on one of the Museum's freight wagons.

Royal Corps of Transport 0–6–0ST 'Woolmer' (1910)

This locomotive was constructed in 1910 for the army by the Avonside Engineering Company of Bristol, to their standard design which dated back to 1889. It was used on the Woolmer Instructional Military Railway in Hampshire until 1919 and was then transferred to another military railway at Hilsea. It is on long-term loan from the Army Transport Museum at Leconfield in North Humberside, and is in its distinctive prussian blue livery.

Southern Railway 4–6–0 Class N15 No. 777 'Sir Lamiel' (1925)

After the formation of the Southern Railway in 1923, R. E. L. Maunsell developed R. W. Urie's Class N15 4–6–0s to meet an urgent demand for additional express passenger locomotives. The rugged two-cylinder design proved capable of hauling fast trains on virtually all of the Southern Railway's main lines. The locomotives were named after the knights of the Round Table, as part of a publicity campaign connecting the railway

10. *Midland Railway 4–4–0 compound No. 1000.*

with the places in the Arthurian legends which it served, the class becoming known as the 'King Arthurs'. They were the first locomotives in Britain to be fitted with smoke-deflector plates. *Sir Lamiel* was one of the class built by the North British Locomotive Company in Glasgow. It worked on the Bournemouth and West of England services for most of its existence, and on one occasion it averaged 69·2 m.p.h. between Salisbury and Waterloo. It has been restored to working order by the Humberside Locomotive Preservation Group.

London Midland & Scottish Railway 2–6–0 Class 5F5P No. 2700 (1926)

The LMS was formed at the Grouping in 1923, and one of the first new classes of locomotive built by that company was a mixed traffic 2–6–0. The design owed a lot to Lancashire & Yorkshire Railway practice, and most of the 245 locomotives in the class operated over the lines that had been part of the railway. They were characterised by the high-pitched, inclined, cylinders with outside motion and massive motion bracket, which gave them their nickname of 'Crabs'. No. 2700 was the first of the class, and originally appeared as No. 13000 in crimson lake livery. After withdrawal in 1966 it spent some years on the Keighley & Worth Valley Railway before coming to York. It was restored to LMS lined black mixed-traffic livery by the Apprentice Training School of British Rail Engineering at Derby.

London Midland & Scottish Railway 0–6–0 Diesel-Mechanical Shunter No. 7401 'John Alcock' (1932)

In 1932 the LMS took delivery of a number of experimental diesel shunters, including this locomotive, which was built by the Hunslet Engine Co. of Leeds (Works No. 1697). After a period in War Department service from 1940, it was returned to the makers in 1945 who then loaned it for industrial use. It was ultimately presented to the Middleton Railway Trust, from whom it is on loan to the Museum. The name *John Alcock* commemorates a Managing Director of the Hunslet Engine Co. and was not carried in LMS days.

Southern Railway 4–4–0 'Schools' Class No. 925 'Cheltenham' (1934)

In 1930 R. E. L. Maunsell produced the largest 4–4–0 design to operate in this country. These were the 'Schools' class, which eventually totalled forty. They were capable of operating over the Hastings line with its restricted clearances, and also worked some of the lighter express trains on the lines to

11. *LNER 2–6–2* Green Arrow *in action on British Rail in 1977.*

12. *LMSR 4–6–2* Duchess of Hamilton.

Bournemouth and the Kent Coast, as well as to Portsmouth before that line was electrified in 1937. *Cheltenham* was built at Eastleigh in 1934, and, when withdrawn in 1962, was chosen for preservation because of its connection with the Railway Correspondence & Travel Society. The locomotive has been restored to the post-war Southern Railway malachite green livery.

Chinese National Railways 4–8–4 No. 607 (1935)
This is an example of the largest non-articulated class of locomotives ever built in this country, weighing 192 tons in working order. It was one of twenty-four, constructed by the Vulcan Foundry to the design of Col. K. Cantlie, and sent to China in 1935–6. They were used on the steeply-graded Canton–Hankow and Nanking–Shanghai lines. Several of the class, including No. 607, were originally fitted with a booster engine on the tender which drove four wheels on one bogie, with coupling rods outside the frames.

The locomotives were withdrawn in the late 1970s and early 1980s. No. 607 was presented to the National Railway Museum by the People's Republic of China during a visit by their Minister of Railways. It arrived in York by road, being 2 ft too high and 1 ft too wide to travel any distance on BR tracks. Restoration to exhibition condition has been financed by the Friends of the National Railway Museum.

London & North Eastern Railway 2–6–2 Class V2 No. 4771 'Green Arrow' (1936)
In the late 1930s Gresley introduced a new class of locomotive designed to work fast freight services, but the 184 members of the class were also widely used for express passenger trains.

Many standard features were built into the locomotive, including the well-known conjugated valve gear for the three-cylinders. The locomotive was restored to working order under the care of Mr D. W. (Bill) Harvey, and has worked a number of special trains on British Railways. It was driven by the Duke of Edinburgh on the occasion of the opening of the Museum on 27 September 1975. It received a boiler overhaul at the Museum in 1977, and in March 1978 it was the locomotive chosen to work the first steam train over the Settle & Carlisle line for nearly ten years.

London Midland & Scottish Railway 'Princess Coronation' 4–6–2 No. 46229 'Duchess of Hamilton' (1938)
The 'Princess Coronation' Pacifics were introduced by William Stainier in 1937 for the 'Coronation Scot' express between Euston and Glasgow. Two of this class produced the highest sustained power output of any steam locomotive recorded in this country, the horsepower achieved being comparable to the 3,300 h.p. (2,460 kW) of a 'Deltic' diesel-electric. In 1939, the LMSR sent the 'Coronation Scot' train to America on exhibition, and *Duchess of Hamilton* was temporarily given the nameplates and number of *Coronation*. The locomotive did not return until after the start of the Second World War. Like the rest of its class, *Duchess of Hamilton* lost its streamlined casing after the war. When the locomotive was withdrawn by British Railways, it was exhibited until early 1975 at Minehead in Butlins Holiday Camp, who then lent it to the Museum. After static restoration by British Rail Engineering Ltd at Swindon to early 1960s livery, it was subsequently restored to steaming condition in 1980, at the expense of the Friends of the National Railway Museum, and is operated by them on BR Specials.

London & North Eastern Railway 4–6–2 Class A4 No. 4468 'Mallard' (1938)

This is probably the most famous locomotive in the National Collection. On 3 July 1938, *Mallard* reached 126 m.p.h. (203 Km/h) descending Stoke Bank – a world speed record for steam locomotives. These streamlined 'Pacifics' were designed by Sir Nigel Gresley in 1935 to work the 'Silver Jubilee', the first of the high-speed trains that were to mark the zenith of steam traction on the railways of this country. After withdrawal from British Railways service as No. 60022 in 1963, the locomotive was restored as nearly as possible to its record-breaking condition. It did not at that time have a corridor tender, but later, like most of the class, it had this feature for use when the locomotives operated the 393-mile (633 Km) non-stop run between King's Cross and Edinburgh. After being displayed at Clapham Museum until its closure in 1973, the locomotive travelled from London to York in April 1975 on its own wheels. It has since been to exhibitions to mark the centenary of York Station and the 125th anniversary of Doncaster Works.

Sectioned Locomotive (rebuilt Southern Railway 'Merchant Navy' Class 4–6–2 No. 35029 'Ellerman Lines') (1949)

This was one of the completely new exhibits for the opening of the National Railway Museum. On the Southern Railway, Mr O. V. S. Bulleid's controversial 'Pacifics' first appeared in 1941 and the thirty members of the 'Merchant Navy' class were extensively rebuilt by British Railways in the late 1950s. *Ellerman Lines* was rescued from Barry scrapyard in 1973, and the work of sectioning was carried out to the specifications of the Museum authorities. Something like 11 tons of metal have been removed from the right-hand side of the locomotive to enable visitors to see the interior construction of the firebox, boiler, smokebox, cylinders, and so on. When resting on its own wheels, the locomotive was more than an inch higher on that side because of the reduced weight on the springs. In the Museum, the engine is supported on two cross girders so that the driving wheels and motion can be rotated to enable visitors to see at close range how they work. Push buttons on the nearby walkway enable visitors to identify different components of the locomotive.

English Electric Type (BR Class 20) Bo-Bo Diesel-Electric No. 20050 (1957)

As D8000, this was the first main-line diesel locomotive to be delivered under the BR 1955 Modernisation Plan. It has a 1000-h.p. (745 kW) V-8 engine driving a generator which feeds the four traction motors, one driving each axle. The cab is at one end with duplicated controls in opposite corners. Other similar locomotives are still at work on BR, usually operating in pairs under the control of a single driver.

Brush Type 2 (BR Class 31) A1A-A1A Diesel-Electric No. D5500 (1957)

D5500 was the first production general-purpose diesel-electric locomotive to be built for British Railways, under their 1955 Modernisation Plan, which envisaged the eventual replace-ment of steam locomotives by diesel and electric traction. Power was originally provided by a 1,250 h.p. (930 kW) Mirrlees twelve-cylinder supercharged engine. Later locomotives had a higher power rating, but during 1960 the diesel engines were changed to the English Electric V12 type of 1,470 h.p. (1,100 kW) Under the 1973 renumbering scheme the locomotive became No. 31018. After withdrawal in 1976 it was restored by British Rail Engineering Ltd at Doncaster to its original livery, and the locomotive has operated on the North Yorkshire Moors Railway.

British Railways Bo-Bo Electric Locomotive No. E5001 (1958)

As part of the Kent Coast electrification scheme on the Southern Region, twenty-four electric locomotives were built at Doncaster Works for use on heavy freight trains, and passenger expresses such as the 'Golden Arrow' and 'Night Ferry'. No E5001 was the second of these locomotives, and was subsequently renumbered 71001. A motor-generator set is contained in the body, with a heavy flywheel which stores energy to enable the locomotive to pass over gaps in the conductor rails. The set also gives improved control characteristics. Ten of the class were rebuilt at Crewe as electro-diesels in 1967–8 for use on the Southampton boat-trains and other similar workings. Changed traffic patterns resulted in the converted locomotives, as well as the originals, being withdrawn.

British Railways Class 9F No. 92220, 'Evening Star' (1960)

This was the last steam locomotive to be built by British Railways and, when it was completed at Swindon in 1960, it was named and given express-passenger livery as well as a copper cap to the chimney. All told, 251 of this class were built from 1954 onwards, being notable because of the use of ten-coupled wheels for the first time on a freight locomotive built by the British main-line railways. They were a very popular design and proved themselves capable, on occasions, of working expresses at more than 90 m.p.h. in addition to their more prosaic everyday duties on heavy mineral and freight trains. *Evening Star* is in main-line operating condition, and at the time of writing is based at Didcot in the care of the Great Western Society.

British Railways Class 84 Bo-Bo Electric No. 84001 (1960)

As No. E3036, this was the first 25,000-volt alternating-current locomotive built by the North British Locomotive Company for the first stages of the London Midland Region electrification, with electrical equipment by GEC Traction. Several different classes with the same wheel arrangement were built to test varying designs of mechanical and electrical equipment.

British Railways Class 03 0–6–0 Diesel-Mechanical Shunter No. 03090 (1960)

This locomotive is a representative of the smaller diesel shunters used by British Railways. It was one of a class of 228 developed by British Railways from a design of the Drewry Car Company. The 204 h.p. (152 kW) Gardner engine provides the

14. *The Brush Type 2 diesel-electric locomotive No. D5500.*

15. Evening Star, *British Railways' last steam locomotive.*

13. Mallard – *World Speed Record holder for steam locomotives.*

16. *The Museum's 'Deltic' diesel-electric locomotive in service on British Rail.*

motive power through a fluid coupling to the five-speed epicyclic gearbox. There is a reversing gearbox combined with the final drive, which enables all five gears to be utilised in either direction of travel. The power is transmitted to the six coupled wheels by a jack-shaft and side rods. No. 03090 was built at Doncaster, and when it was withdrawn by BR in 1976 it was claimed as a historical relic under the 1968 Transport Act. It is in full working order and is regularly used to move large exhibits around the Museum or the Peter Allen Building.

English Electric 'Deltic' Co-Co Diesel-Electric No. 55002 'King's Own Yorkshire Light Infantry' (1961)
From 1961 until early 1982 the 3,300-h.p. (2,460 kW) 'Deltic' locomotives were familiar sights on the East Coast Main Line passing the Museum. Within fourteen years, each of the twenty-four locomotives had run two million miles, and the total mileage for the class was over sixty million. The locomotives, with their top speed of 100 m.p.h. (160 Km/h) were responsible for major improvements in East Coast schedules, including the 'Hull Executive', which at one time averaged over 91 m.p.h. (146 Km/h) from King's Cross to Retford. Although the prototype of the class is on display in the Science Museum, the NRM claimed one of the service locomotives when it was withdrawn in December 1981. No. 55002 had been earmarked earlier, having been chosen because of its general condition and the Yorkshire regimental association. For its final thirteen months in service it was painted in its original colours with the aid of a grant by the Friends of the National Railway Museum.

British Railways Class 02 0–4–0 Diesel Shunter No. D2860 (1961)
This locomotive was one of a class of diesel-hydraulic shunters with 170 h.p. (125 kW) Rolls-Royce engines, built for British Railways by the Yorkshire Engine Company of Sheffield during 1960–1. No. D2860 is used for shunting purposes in the Museum. Its wheelbase is only 6 ft (187 cm), which enables it to negotiate curves of as little as 60 ft (18 m) radius.

British Railways Class 52 C-C Diesel-Hydraulic No. D1023 'Western Fusilier' (1963)
Hydraulic, rather than electric, transmission was used extensively on the Western Region of British Railways, and this particular class was the most powerful of their designs. Thirty of the class, including No. D1023, were built at Swindon, the remainder coming from Crewe. Two 1,380 h.p. (1,030 kW) Bristol-Siddeley Maybach twelve-cylinder engines are installed. Each drives the three axles on its own bogie through a Voith gearbox. This contains three torque converters which are filled with oil, one at a time, to obtain the appropriate gear ratio for the speed of the train. The locomotives have a very high tractive effort of 72,000 lb (320 kN) which was intended to help them deal with the steep gradients found in the West of England. The 'Westerns', like all the diesel-hydraulic locomotives, proved expensive in maintenance, and were phased out, *Western Fusilier* being one of the last to be withdrawn, in February 1977. It has been restored to its original maroon livery, and remains in full working order, running in service on the Torbay & Dartmouth Railway in 1981–2.

Industrial Locomotives

The Locomotive Collection, as inherited by the National Railway Museum from British Railways, only covered types that had been used by the main-line railway companies. However, in the days of steam there were approximately as many privately-owned locomotives at work in mines, quarries and factories. Accordingly the Museum is building up a small collection of these locomotives chosen from the seventy different companies which built locomotives of this sort. The following locomotives are expected to be at York, but not necessarily on display.

Hunslet Engine Co. 0–4–0 Steam Saddle-tank 'Hodbarrow' (1882)
This locomotive was built by the Hunslet Engine Company of Leeds (Works Number 299) for the Hodbarrow Mining Company in Cumberland in 1882, to a ten-year-old design. It remained at work until shortly before the mines closed in the 1960s, having been reboilered in 1919. It was preserved by its makers, who are still in business as builders of locomotives, and is on loan to the Museum. It is being restored by the Friends of the National Railway Museum.

Armstrong Whitworth & Co. 0–4–0 Diesel-Electric No. D21 (1933)
During the early 1930s, the firm of Armstrong Whitworth & Co. on Tyneside realised the potential of diesel-electric traction and built a number of different locomotives and railcars. This is the first of six such shunting engines built in 1933, and was used at Dunston Power Station until the early 1970s. The diesel is loaned to the Museum by the Hexham Rolling Stock Group. A very similar locomotive was used for passenger and freight services on the North Sunderland Railway.

Robert Stephenson & Hawthorns Ltd 0–4–0 Steam Saddle-tank Dunston Power Station No. 15 (1942)
This locomotive is typical of those built by Robert Stephenson & Hawthorns Ltd at Newcastle upon Tyne (Works number 7603). The large unsprung 'dumb' buffers stand up to the frequent impacts and prevent 'buffer-locking'. It is on loan to the Museum from the Hexham Rolling Stock Group.

Stephenson-Crossley 360 h.p. 0–6–0 Diesel-Mechanical Shunter No. 3 (1954)
This is an example of a pre-Second World War design of heavy-duty diesel shunter with mechanical transmission. Reversing is achieved by stopping the two-stroke engine, rotating the camshaft and restarting with the aid of compressed air. The locomotive was used at Carrington Power Station, between Manchester and Warrington.

Andrew Barclay 0–4–0 Fireless Locomotive 'Imperial No. 1' (1956)
In certain types of location, the fire of an ordinary steam locomotive could present a hazard, and under such conditions fireless locomotives were often used. The 'boiler' was in fact a large pressure vessel which was replenished with steam at intervals from the factory mains. The driver could admit steam from this reservoir to the cylinders, a reducing valve preventing the tractive effort from getting too high. This locomotive was the last-but-one fireless locomotive to be built by Andrew Barclay (Works Number 2373). It worked at the Imperial Paper Mills at Gravesend and was presented to the Museum by Mr A. G. Wilton.

Sentinel 0–4–0 Steam Locomotive 'Tees-side No. 5' (1957)
In the 1900s the engineering firm of Alley & MacLellan of Glasgow started building steam road wagons, using high-speed reciprocating engines and chain drives, together with a special design of vertical boiler. In the 1920s, they built a considerable number of railway locomotives, based on these features, for industrial purposes and for main-line use, as well as some steam railcars. This locomotive, built in 1957 (Works Number 9679), was purchased from the British Steel Corporation by Mr J. F. G. MacLagan and presented to the Museum.

The Museum

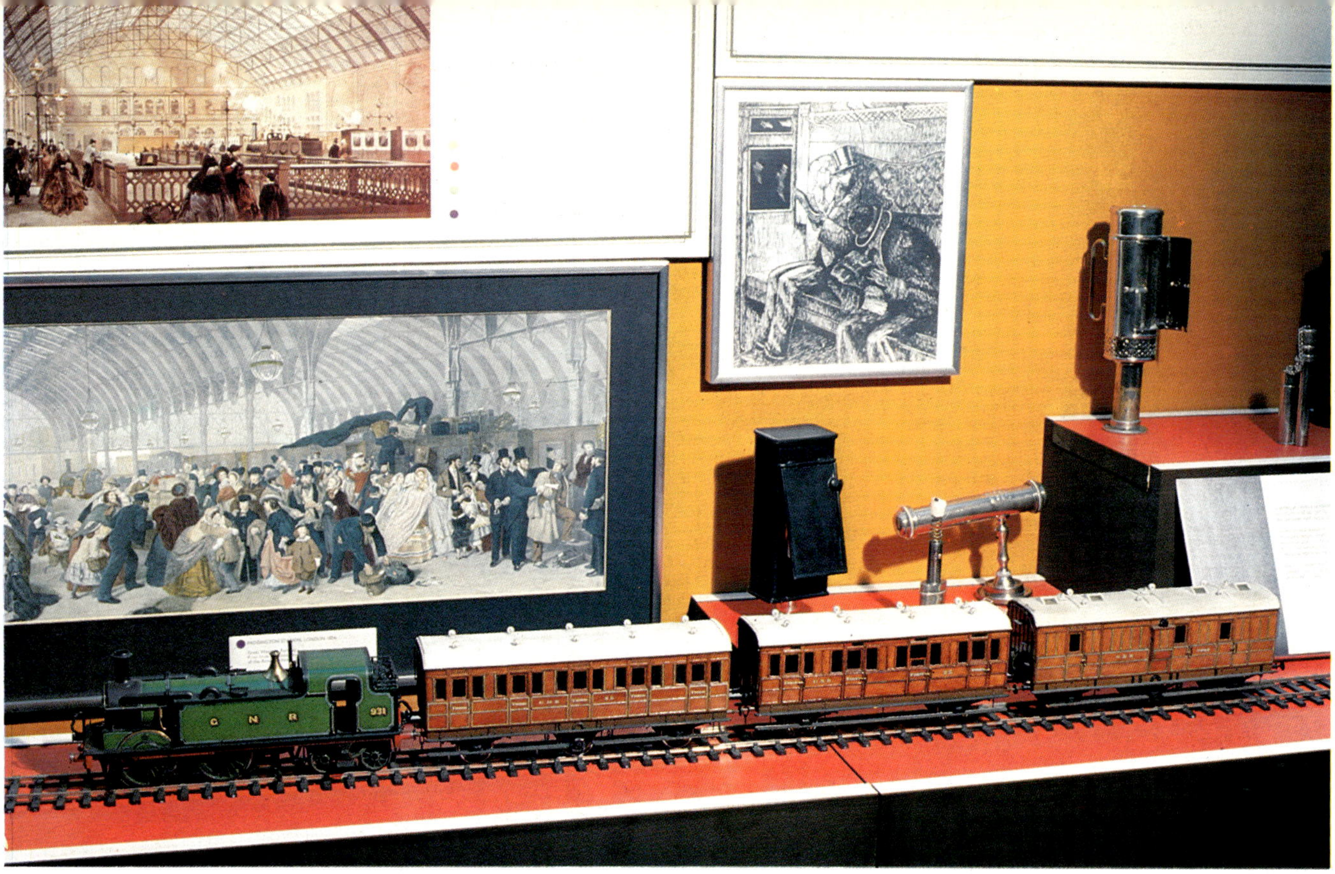
G N R
931

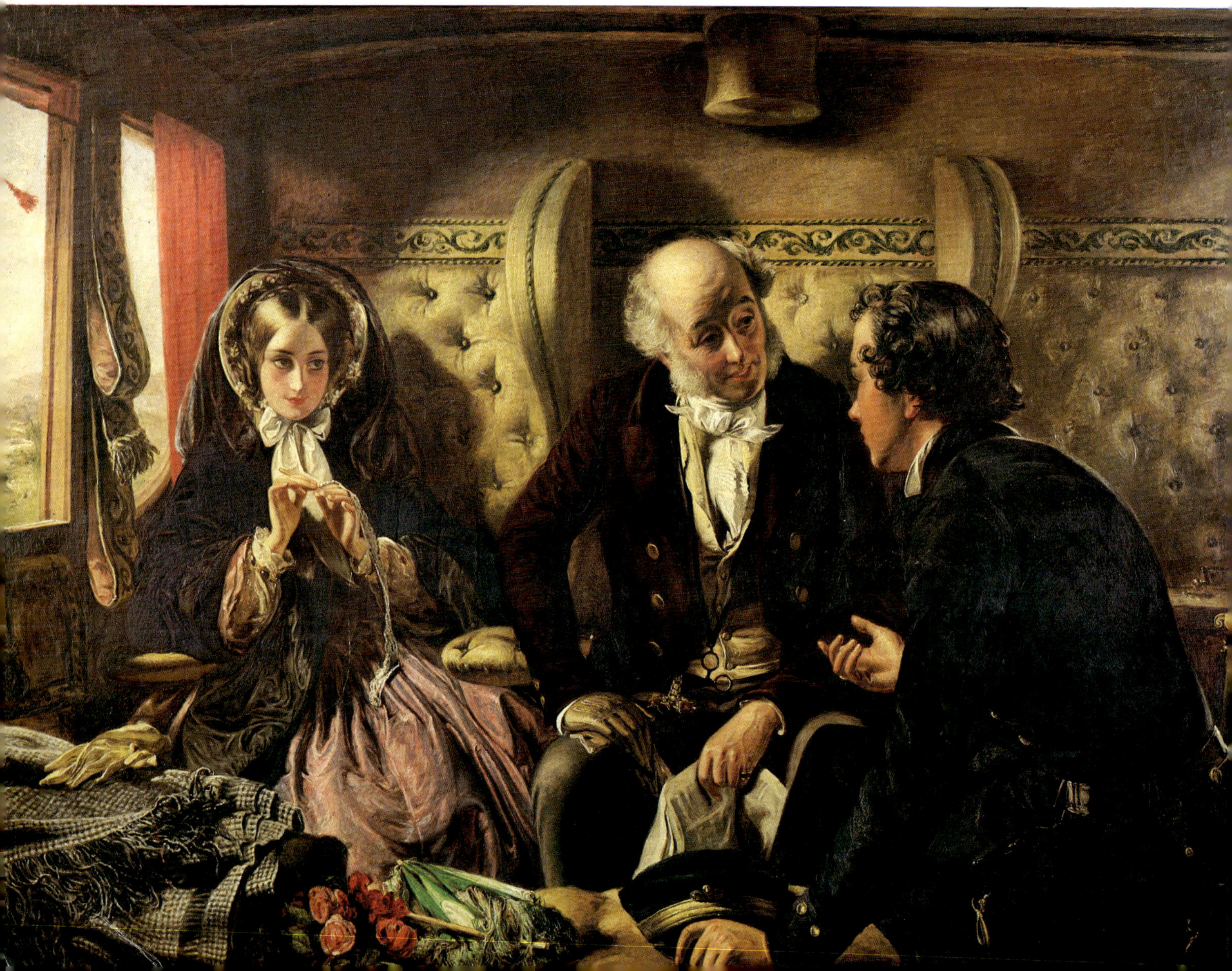

20

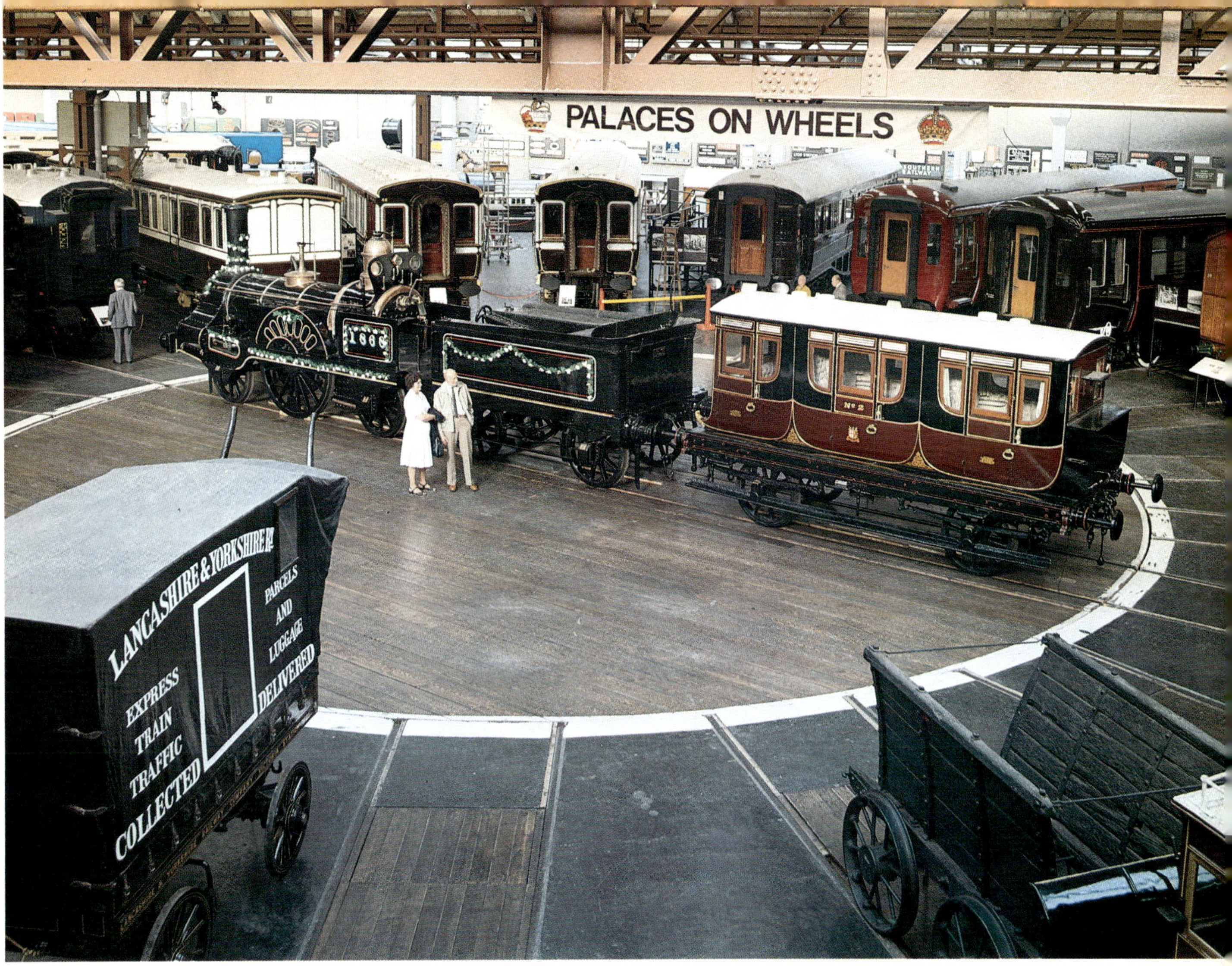

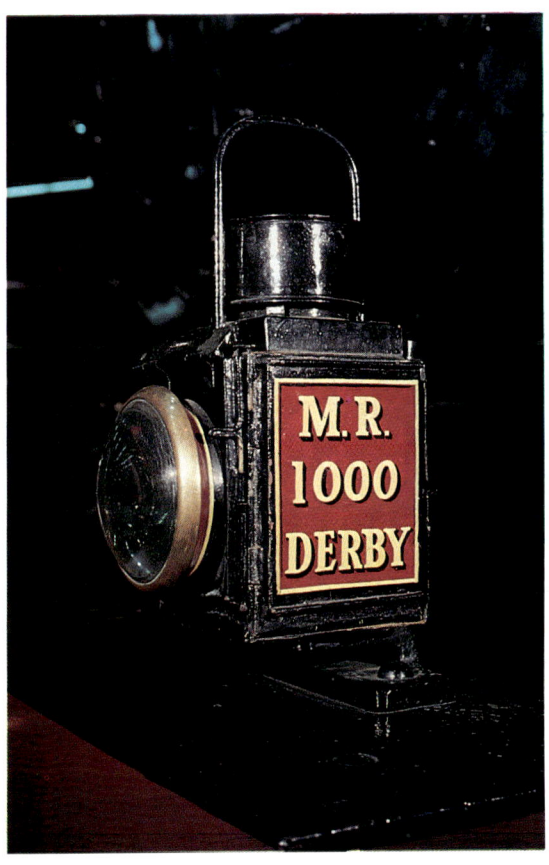

18. *A section of a Balcony showcase.*

19. The Return – First-Class; *one of the nineteenth-century paintings in the collection.*

20. *Special Exhibition on 'B' turntable.*

21. *Locomotive headlamp.*

22. *Express train headboards.*

19 21 22

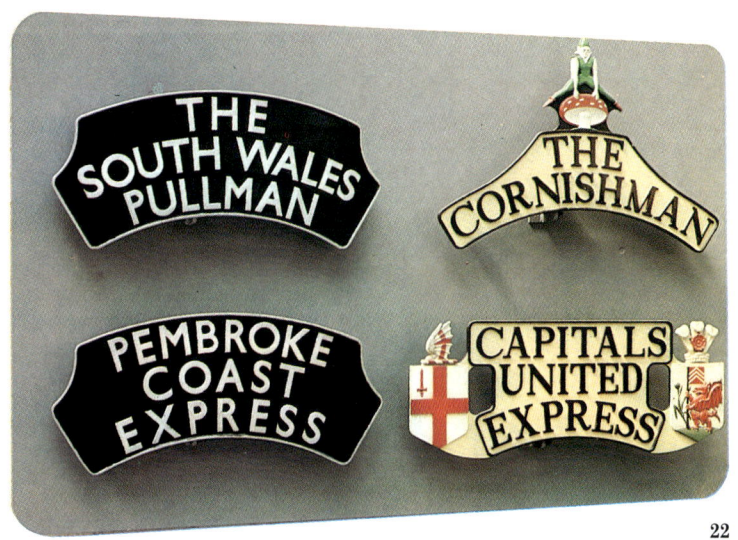

23

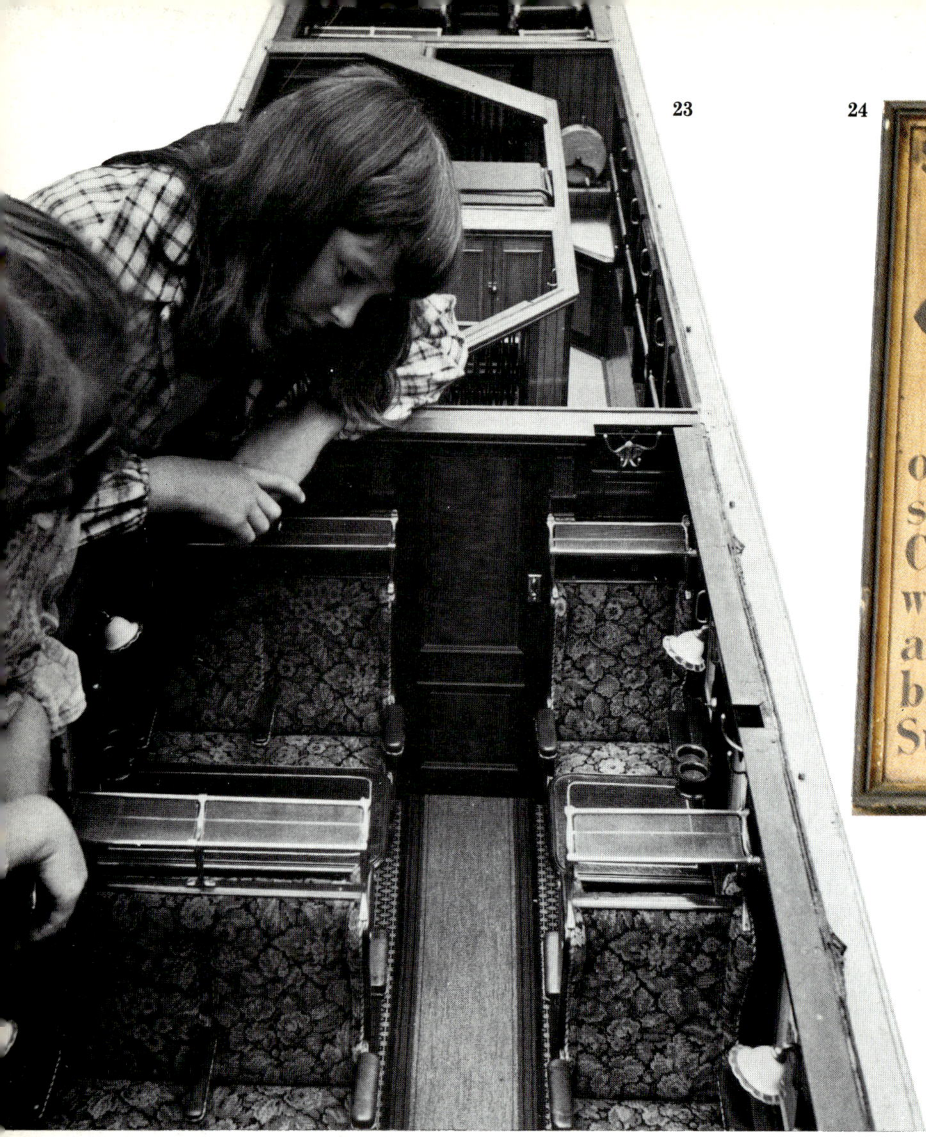

24

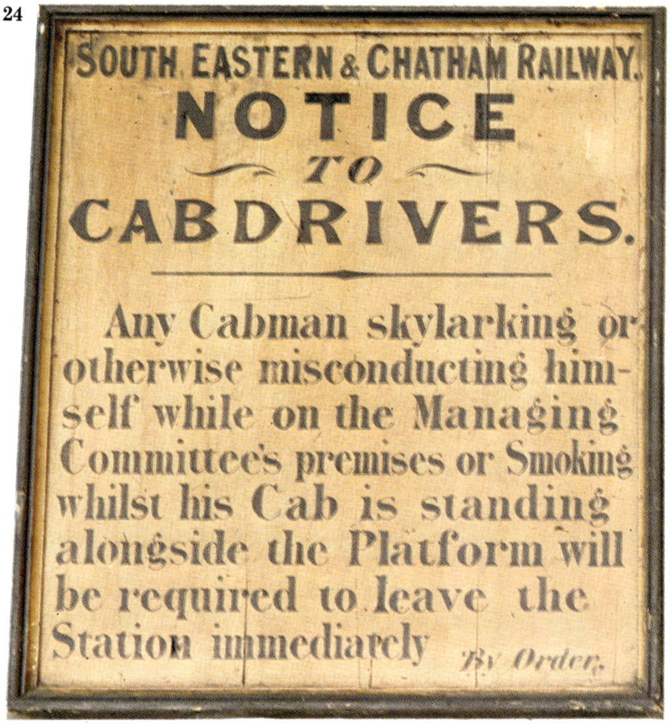
SOUTH EASTERN & CHATHAM RAILWAY.
NOTICE
TO
CABDRIVERS.
Any Cabman skylarking or otherwise misconducting himself while on the Managing Committee's premises or Smoking whilst his Cab is standing alongside the Platform will be required to leave the Station immediately
By Order.

23. *The wonders of the craftsman's skill.*
24. *Disciplinary measures.*
25. *Some of the Museum's 'Railwayana'.*
26. *Example of enamel sign from a station.*
27. *Cab of* Mallard.
28. *Commemorative plaque on* Mallard.
29. *The Reference Library.*

GENTLEMEN'S
ROOM

26

TAFF VALE RAILWAY COMPANY 1836
North Staffordshire Railway Company
LONDON TILBURY & SOUTHEND RAILWAY
THE DONEGAL RAILWAY COMPANY
TYRCONNEL

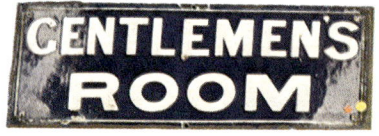

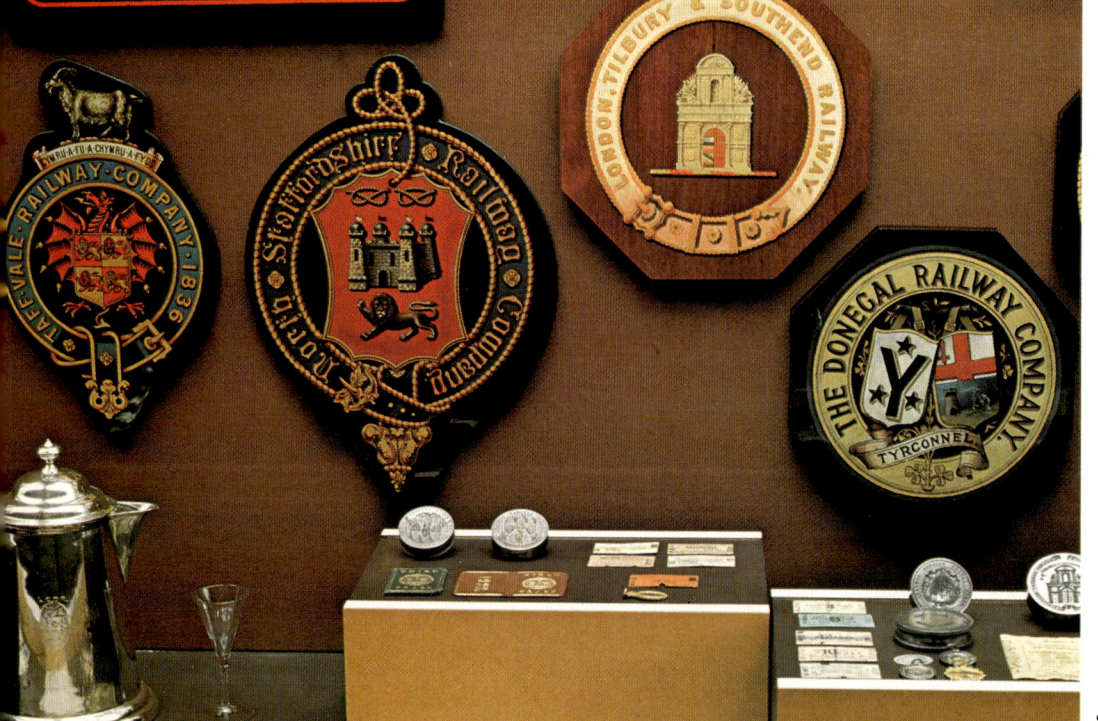

25

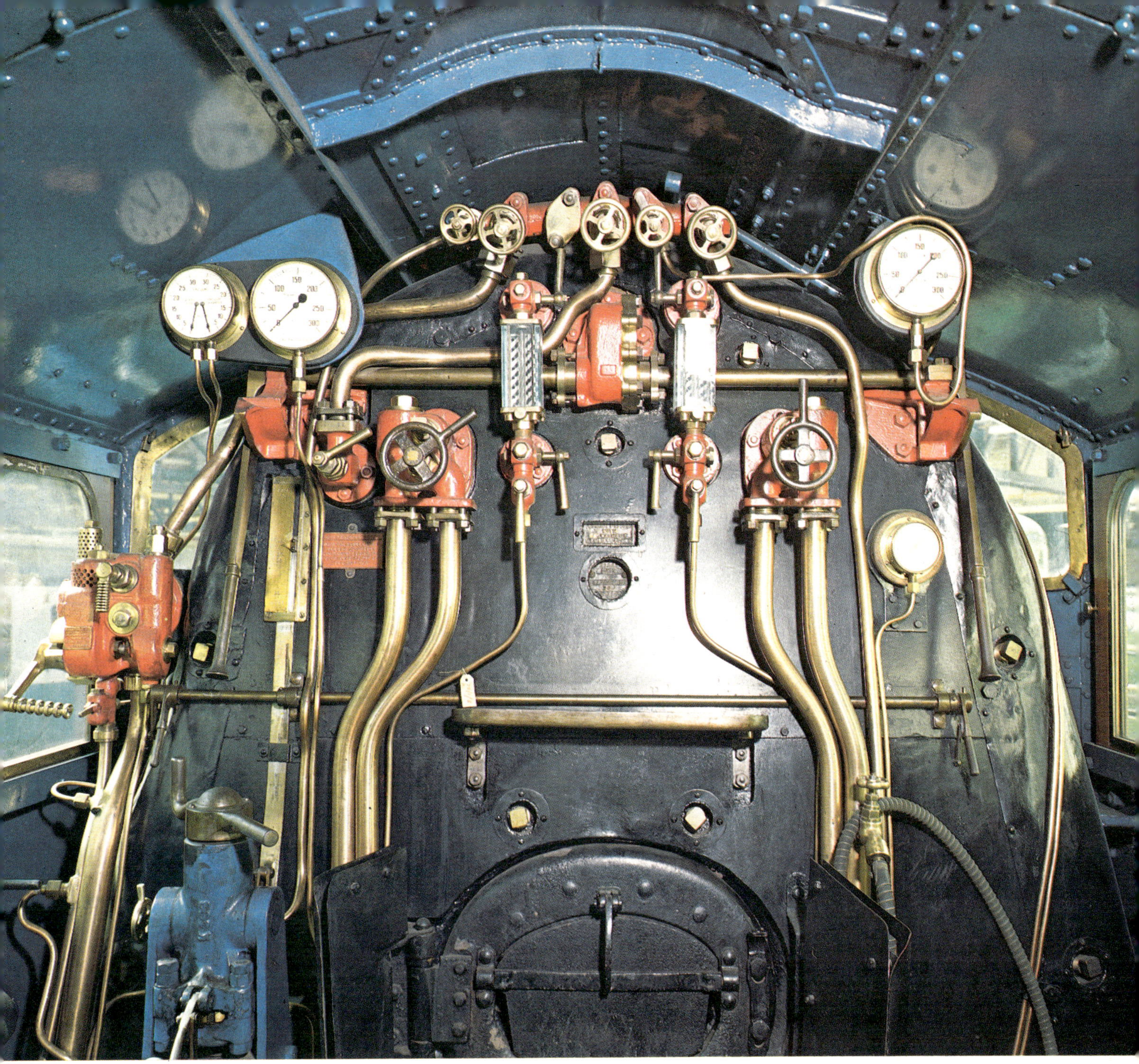

27

LNER
ON
3RD JULY 1938
THIS LOCOMOTIVE
ATTAINED A
WORLD SPEED RECORD
FOR STEAM TRACTION
OF 126
MILES PER HOUR

28

FIRE EXIT →

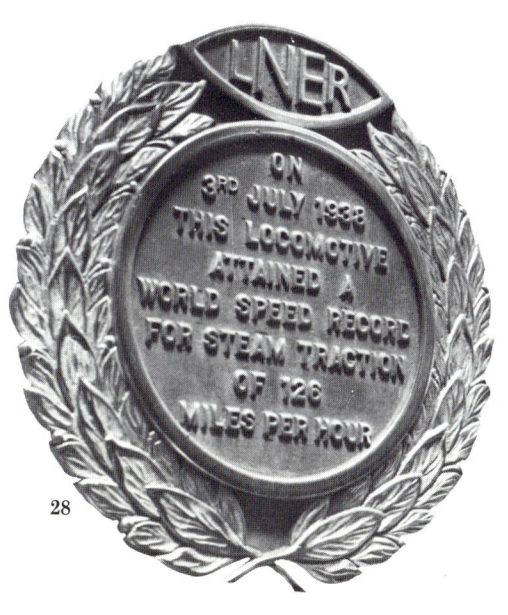

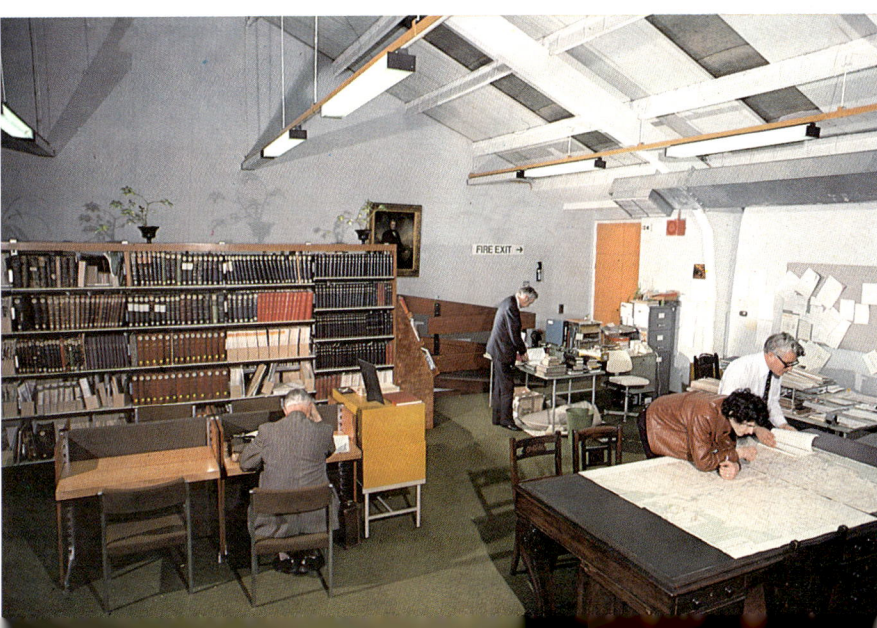

29

30. *Belvoir Castle wagon.*

31. *'Totem' style station nameboards (early British Railways).*

32. *'Old Coppernob' and the Weatherhill engine.*

33. *Southern Region electric locomotive.*

34. *South Eastern & Chatham Railway 4–4–0 No. 737 over illuminated deep pit to view underneath of locomotive.*

35. *Part of the Signalling Exhibition used for demonstrations.*

34

35

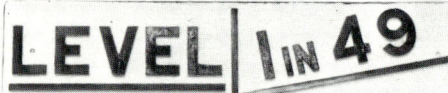

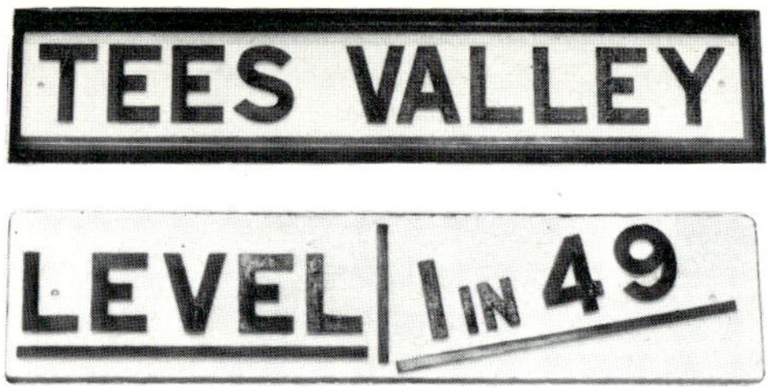
TEES VALLEY
LEVEL
1 IN 49

36. *North Eastern Railway signal box and gradient signs.*

37. *The statue of George Stephenson, originally displayed in the old station at Euston.*

38. *How it works – the sectioned 'Pacific' locomotive* Ellerman Lines.

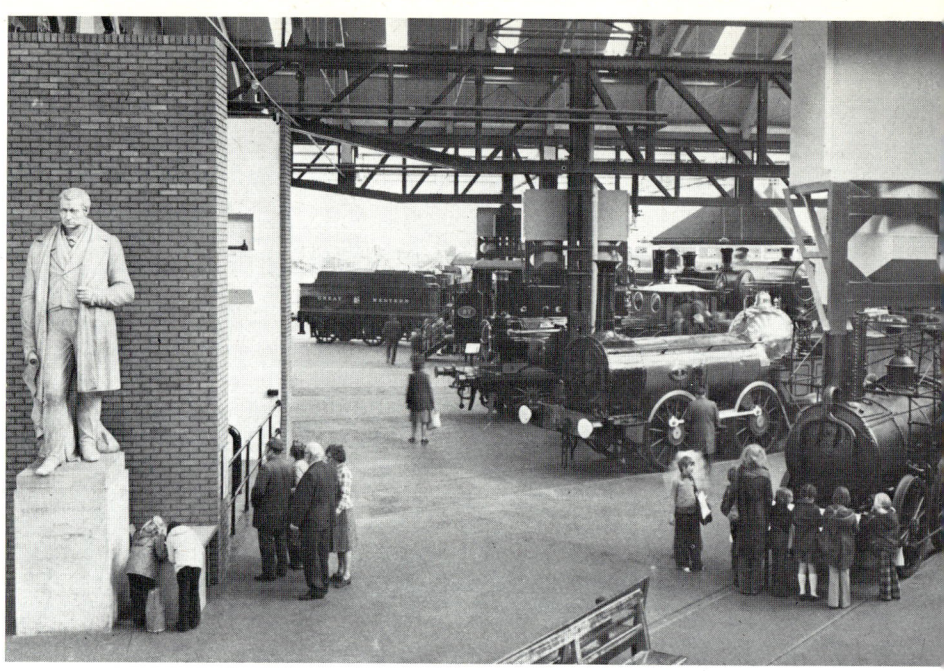

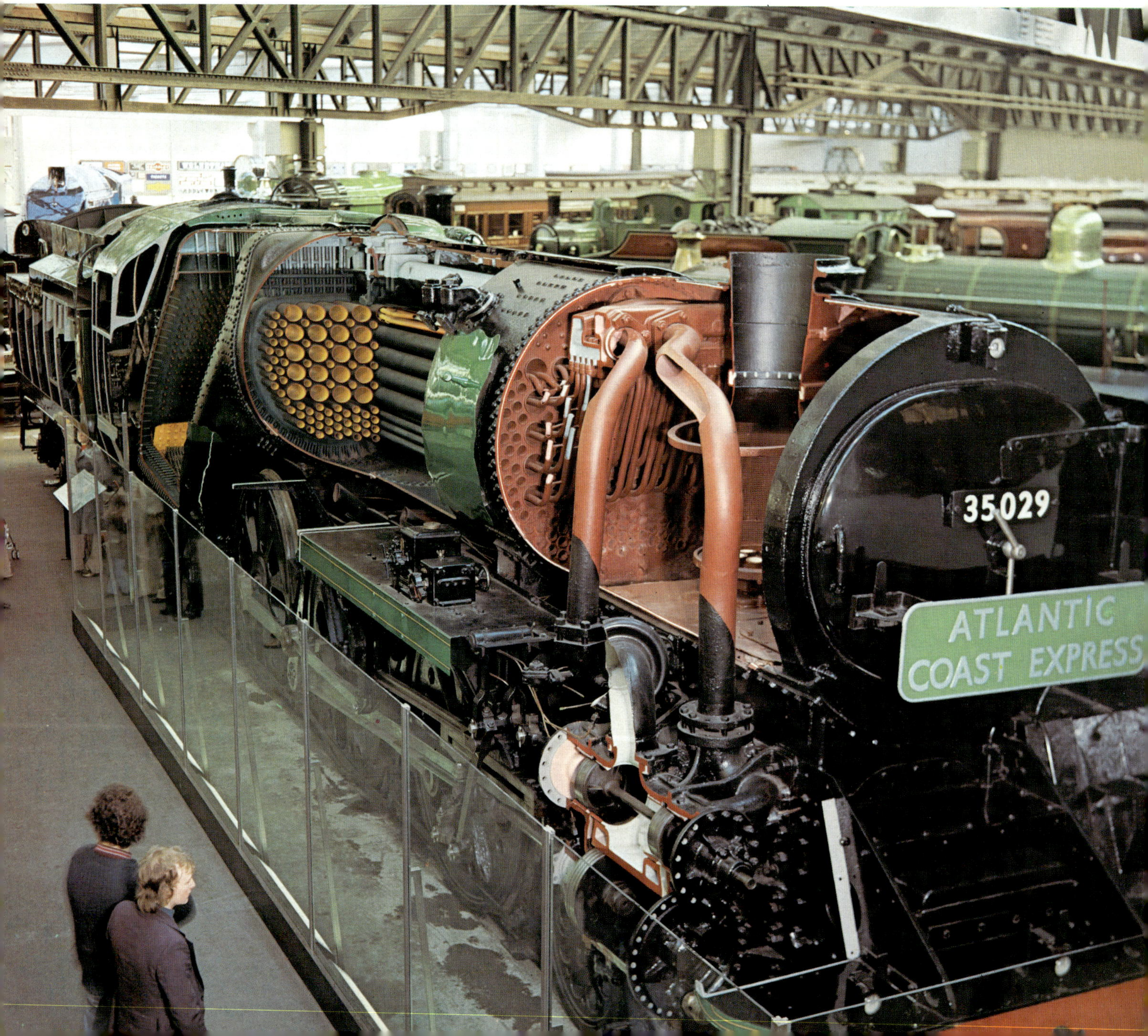
35029
ATLANTIC
COAST EXPRESS

37

39

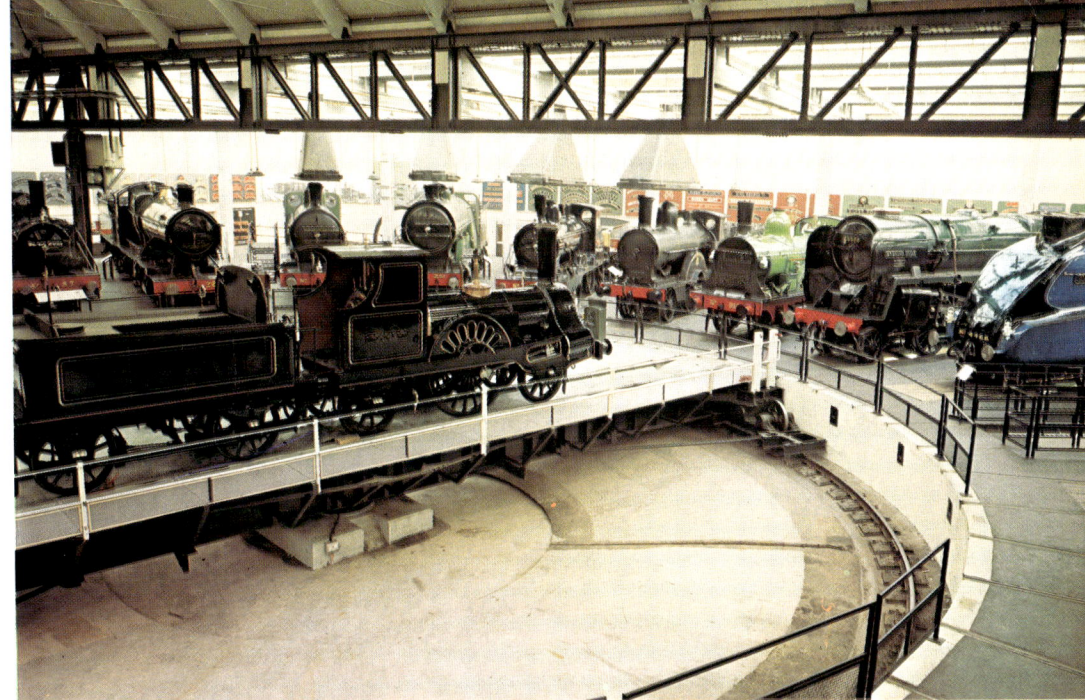

39. *The 'A' turntable.*

40. *Their Royal Highnesses the Prince and Princess of Wales alight from one of the Edwardian Royal Saloons during their visit to the Museum in November 1981.*

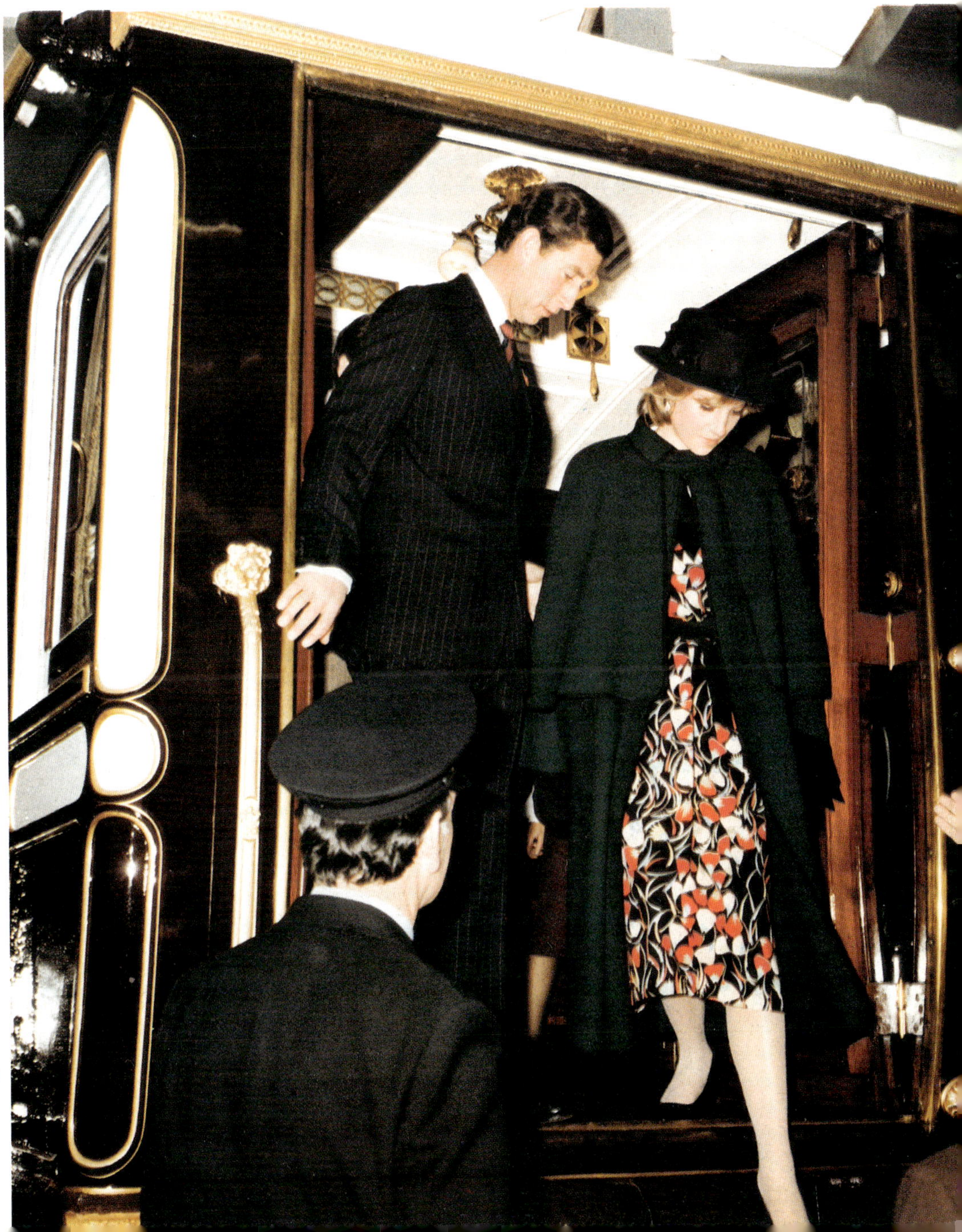

38

40

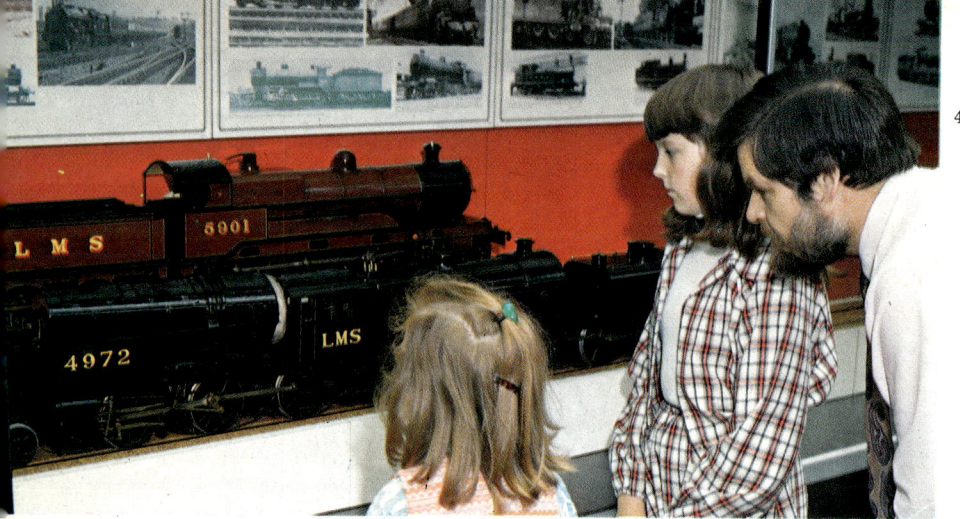

41

L M S
5901
4972
LMS

42

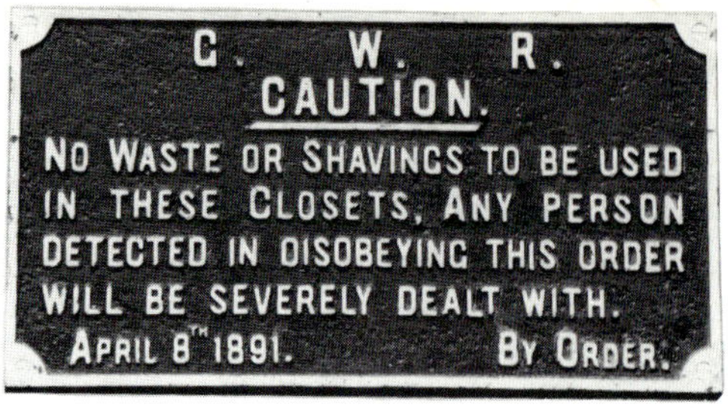
G. W. R.
CAUTION.
NO WASTE OR SHAVINGS TO BE USED
IN THESE CLOSETS, ANY PERSON
DETECTED IN DISOBEYING THIS ORDER
WILL BE SEVERELY DEALT WITH.
APRIL 8TH 1891.
BY ORDER.

41. *The Museum is planned for visitors of all ages.*

42. *A cautionary notice.*

43. *Great Eastern Railway locomotive number-plate.*

44. *The motion of* Duchess of Hamilton.

43

GREAT EASTERN RAILWAY CO.
490
STRATFORD WORKS 1894

44

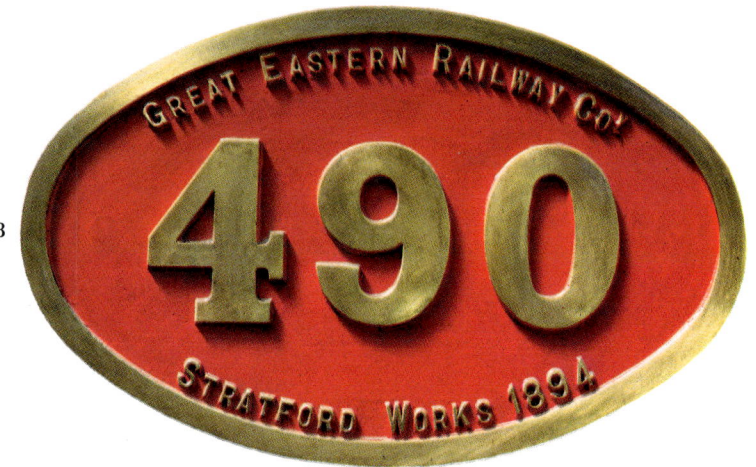

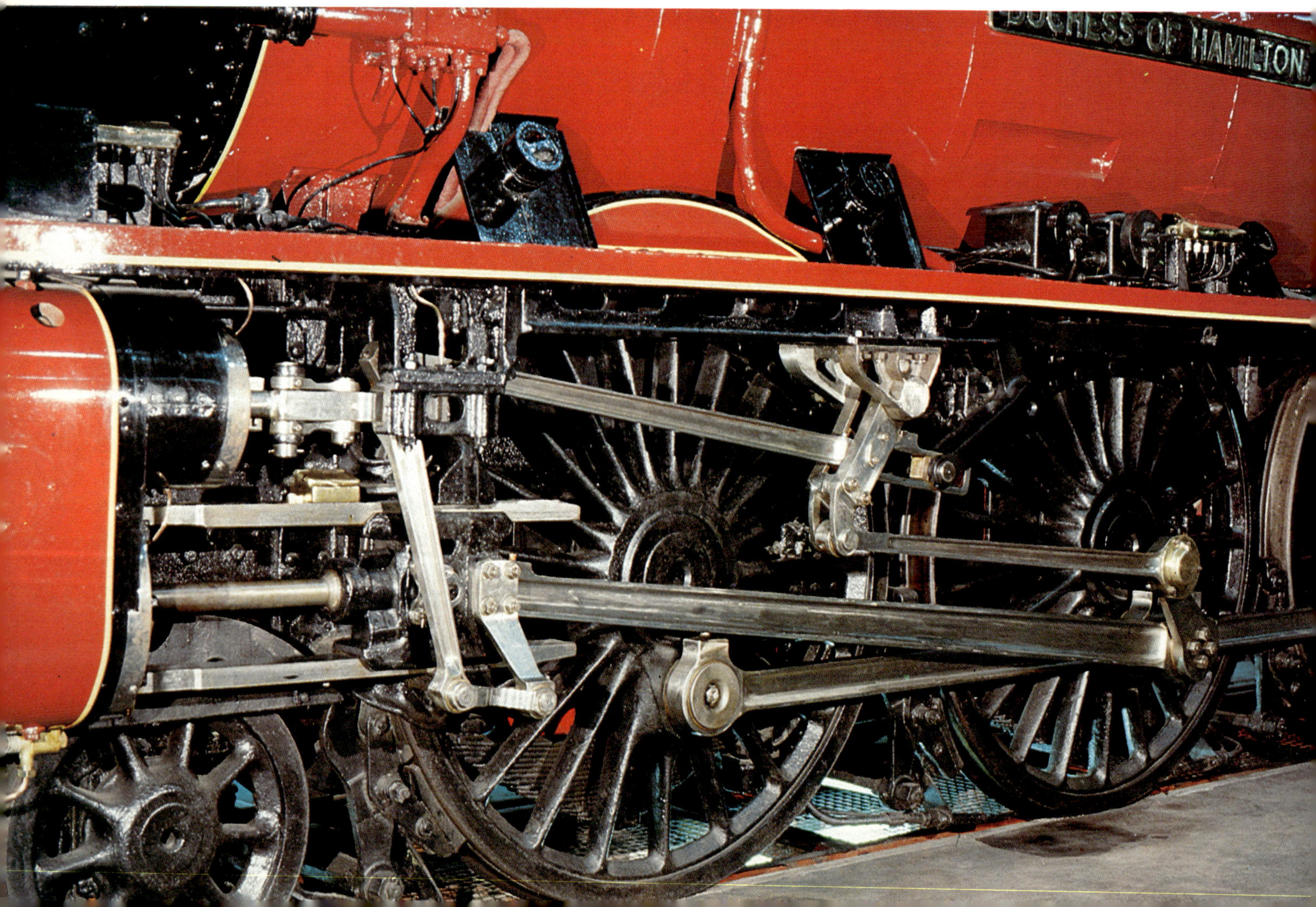
DUCHESS OF HAMILTON

45. *Locomotives from the gallery.*
46. *The Front Gallery.*
47. *The Lecture Theatre – available for school and other parties by prior arrangement.*
48. *Bridge warning notice.*

46

47

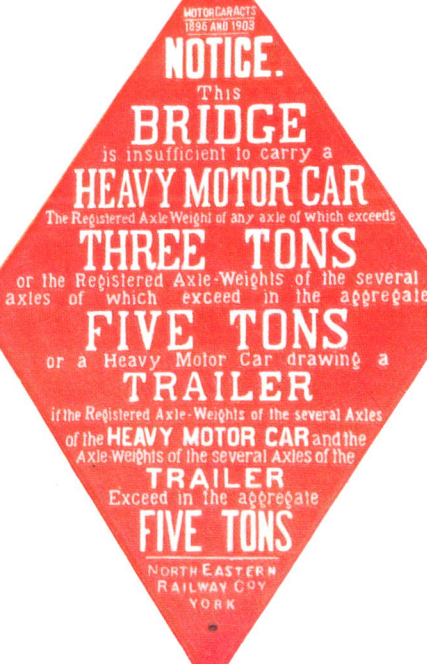

48

49. The Chinese National Railways 4–8–4 No. 607 is unloaded in the Thames after its return to this country.

50. Lancashire & Yorkshire Railway passenger tank No. 1008.

51, 52. Wax figures showing period uniforms.

52

53. London & North Western Railway Saloon for Queen Victoria, originally dating from 1869.

Rolling Stock

Coaching Stock
including powered passenger vehicles

Bodmin & Wadebridge Railway Carriages (1830s)
The building dates of these three coaches are uncertain, but their underframes are believed to date from the late 1830s, although the bodies are probably of rather later construction. The London & South Western Railway did not link up with its subsidiary, the Bodmin & Wadebridge, until the 1880s, and when the carriage superintendent saw these ancient vehicles he fortunately realised their historical importance and ordered their preservation. They have wooden bodies with oak frames and pine panelling. The buffers are of the 'dumb' type without any form of springing to take up the shock.

Liverpool & Manchester Railway Replica Coaches (1834)
Three pairs of full-size replicas were built in 1930 to commemorate the centenary of the opening of the Liverpool & Manchester Railway. The yellow vehicles are first-class coaches with three wholly-enclosed compartments. The body styling owes much to the design of contemporary road coaches. The open second-class vehicles are little more than boxes on wheels, and present a standard of travelling comparable to that enjoyed by the 'outside' passengers on the road stage coaches at the time.

Travelling Post Office Replica (1838)
This exhibit represents the first purpose-built Travelling Post Office, as constructed for the Grand Junction Railway. There is a sorting bench along half the length of one side opposite the net, while above the bench there are pigeon holes for sorting the mail. This reconstruction has been mounted on an underframe of unknown origin, so that it may not display the authentic details of the original vehicles, but it does represent an important milestone in the railways' handling of mail.

Queen Adelaide's Coach, London & Birmingham Railway (1842)
This coach is correctly described as a 'bed-carriage', and is of a type initially built by the London & Birmingham Railway in 1837 for ordinary first-class passengers. By using poles, webbing and stiff cushions, a bed could be made up at night, with the passengers' feet projecting into the 'boot' at one end. This particular vehicle, with rather more purpose-built arrangements, was intended for the widow of King William IV. It is finished in a far more elaborate manner than ordinary first-class vehicles, the bodywork being by Hooper, later known for their connections with Daimler and Rolls-Royce motor cars. The handles are gold plated and the armorial bearings were hand painted since transfers were not at that time generally available.

Stockton & Darlington Railway Composite Carriage No. 59 (1846)
By the 1840s the first experimental period of railway carriage construction was reaching its close, most standard-gauge systems in Britain having adopted a three-compartment, four-wheel design such as this example from the pioneering Stockton & Darlington Railway. The central first-class compartment is far better furnished and decorated than the second-class one on each side of it. The latter were, however, infinitely better than the accommodation provided for the guard, who rode on a seat at one end of the roof. From this perch he had to climb down to apply the brakes whenever the engine driver whistled instructions. Luggage was also carried on the roof.

The exterior of one end and one side of the vehicle has been restored by having the old varnish removed by Museum staff, using picture-restoration techniques.

North British Railway Port Carlisle 'Dandy-Cart' (1861)
This unusual horse-drawn vehicle was used between 1861 and 1914 for the passenger service on the short branch of the North British Railway from Drumburgh to Port Carlisle. First- and second-class passengers travelled inside, while the third-class passengers were perched outside with their backs to the carriage and their feet on the foot boards. Luggage was carried on the roof. In 1914 steam took over until the line was closed in 1932. The vehicle was rescued and restored in 1925, and was subsequently exhibited at various places before coming to the National Railway Museum in 1975. Since then it has been restored to its present external livery (c. 1900), and the original end windows, which had disappeared during its operational lifetime, were replaced.

Queen Victoria's Saloon; London & North Western Railway (1869)
This elaborate saloon was reputedly Queen Victoria's favourite railways vehicle, having been built jointly at her and the railway's expense, and was not replaced until after her death. Most of her long-distance journeys were over the London & North Western, and Caledonian Railways, and the West Coast Route consequently developed a proprietorial interest in the operation of the Royal Train. This vehicle started life as two separate six-wheel vehicles connected by a flexible gangway, the first to be fitted to coaches in this country. In 1890, the rigid wheelbases were altered by the use of one of Webb's radial axleboxes on each vehicle (as on the West Coast Joint Stock TPO). After five years in this form, the two bodies were remounted on a new twelve-wheel bogie underframe, which gave better riding and overcame the Queen's dislike of having to pass from one vehicle to the other while it was in motion. It was not until after the accession of King Edward VII that this vehicle was replaced in the Royal Train by the two newer saloons also in the Museum collection. Because of their great age, the silk fabrics used inside the vehicle are exceedingly fragile.

North London Railway Directors' Inspection Saloon (1872)
Although built for a special purpose, this vehicle was generally similar to contemporary general-service North London Railway coaches. Its body is constructed entirely of teak, which, because of its natural oily character, is more resistant to weathering than other timbers. This particular vehicle is a fine example of the use of this timber, which has been selected and finished with special care because of its important role on the railway. It has an open saloon with lavatories at one end and an attendant's compartment at the other. It is furnished in a combination of tapestry and mahogany, with lincrusta ceilings and roller blinds.

Midland Railway Six-Wheel Composite Carriage (1885)
This vehicle is typical of Midland Railway carriage construction from the late 1870s until the late 1890s when its famous clerestory coaches were first constructed. It was restored for exhibition at the National Railway Museum by British Rail Engineering Limited at Wolverton. This involved, among other things, the weaving of special lengths of braid for the seats, and the production of new transfers of the Midland Railway armorial device. The coach is finished in the Midland livery of crimson lake, dating from about 1883. The absence of any second-class accommodation is a reminder that the Midland abolished this class of travel during the 1870s and up-rated the standards used in the third-class compartments.

West Coast Joint Stock Travelling Post Office (1885)
This is the oldest surviving British example of a travelling Post Office coach, although it is not in its original form. It was built at Wolverton and is painted in standard LNWR livery, but carries the insignia of the West Coast Joint Stock, to indicate its joint ownership by the LNWR and Caledonian Railway. Equipment is provided for collecting and dropping off bags of mail without the train stopping. As with many subsequent TPO vehicles, the gangway connections are offset at the ends of the coaches to enable maximum use to be made of the interior for sorting equipment. It is not a bogie vehicle. The centre axles are rigid and the other ones are on radial slides.

Great Northern Railway Six-Wheeled Brake Van (1887)
This vehicle is typical of the standard passenger train vehicles

54. *Queen Adelaide's Coach (1842).*

of the Great Northern Railway as built in large numbers between 1876 and 1896. This particular vehicle remained in ordinary use until the 1930s, when it was converted first of all to be a travelling stores van and later for use in a breakdown train. It was taken out of service finally in the 1960s, and has been restored to its original livery by British Rail Engineering Ltd at York to the Museum's specifications.

East Coast Joint Stock Corridor Third-Class Coach No. 12 (1898)

This example of late Victorian coachbuilding exemplifies the standard of ordinary passenger accommodation achieved on the more prestigious long-distance services at the turn of the century. The coach was built for the East Coast Joint Stock – the vehicles used for through services – and jointly owned by the Great Northern, North Eastern and North British Railways. Although constructed at the York Works of the NER, it more closely follows Great Northern styling. This, in turn, after the replacement of the clerestory roof by a full elliptical version, became characteristic of the GNR and LNER under Nigel Gresley. The vehicle is an early example of a coach with continuous gangway communication along the vehicle – an uncommon feature on many British railways until well into the twentieth century. Although finished in ECJS colours, it is trimmed with LNER pattern upholstery.

The Duke of Sutherland's Private Saloon (1899)

This privately-owned coach was built by the LNWR for the 4th Duke of Sutherland. He had the right to run his own private carriage and locomotive over all lines north of Inverness, and this vehicle was used to entertain members of many European Royal Families. It was fully equipped to run on the other main-line railways at the turn of the century, and provide self-contained hotel facilities for its owner wherever he wished to travel. It is generally considered to have been the prototype for the Royal Saloons constructed three years later for King

Edward VII and Queen Alexandra. Since the opening of the Museum, this saloon has made several special journeys over British Railways' tracks.

London & North Western Railway First-Class Dining Saloon No. 76 (1900)

This vehicle was originally built as one of the West Coast Joint Stock dining coaches, but shortly after its construction it went to Paris for exhibition, where it was awarded a Grand Prix. By 1904 it had been permanently allocated for use in the Royal Train. As built, it had single seats in dining saloons for twenty passengers, but in its present form, dating from 1942, the individual chairs in the smaller saloon are arranged round a centre table. In 1938, the vehicle was given an LMS-pattern underframe to replace the original LNWR one. It nevertheless retains much that is typical of LNWR practice, notably the elaborate entrance vestibules, the domed clerestory ends and much of the interior finish. In 1978 it was repainted at the Wolverton Works of British Rail Engineering Ltd in the 1937 Royal Train livery, which was essentially the LNWR colours with LMS markings.

London & North Western Railway Royal Saloons (1902)

While Queen Victoria did not want to change her 1869 Royal Saloon, by the turn of the century the LNWR was very anxious to build something new, and so, after King Edward VII's accession in 1901, Mr C. A. Park, the LNWR Carriage Superintendent, enquired whether His Majesty would approve the construction of a new train. The King was enthusiastic, and the two vehicles built for him and Queen Alexandra represent the finest period of British railway carriage construction. This was when the railways generally were at their most influential and prosperous.

The vehicles were originally painted in the traditional LNWR livery of carmine lake and white, with the addition of some rather more elaborate gold lining, and this was retained in LMS days. At the beginning of the Second World War they were considered to be too prominent from the air, and were repainted in the standard LMS crimson. Both vehicles have been repainted in their 1938 livery, the cost of the work on Queen Alexandra's being met by the Friends of the National Railway Museum. The interiors of the day saloons in the two vehicles were re-upholstered during King George V's reign, but some idea of the original furnishings can be obtained from the quarter-scale model of the King's Saloon which is exhibited nearby.

London & South Western Railway Tri-Composite Brake No. 3598 (1903)

This vehicle typifies the British non-corridor ordinary coach of the late Victorian/Edwardian period. Three classes of passenger were carried in this particular example and there was also space for the guard and luggage, this arrangement being useful for through carriages on branch lines. Other matching 'one class only' coaches were also built both with and without a guard's van. It will be noted that, even though no corridor is present, all passengers still can gain access to the lavatories, situated between adjacent compartments. Not all coaches of this type were, however, thus equipped, especially those used on shorter-distance services. The coach passed to the Southern Railway in 1923 and the upholstery is of this company's patterns.

Royal Train First-Class Corridor Brakes Nos. 5154/5 (1905)

These coaches were built as first-class ordinary vehicles by the London & North Western Railway at Wolverton Works, and subsequently were rebuilt to match the rest of the Royal Train for use as staff vehicles. They contained a variety of ancillary equipment to service the Royal Train, but the interior compartment furnishing remains essentially typical of normal general service coaches of the Edwardian period. After being given new underframes by the LMS in 1937, the vehicles remained in use until the new Royal Train came into service in 1977. Before arriving at York, the coaches were repainted in their 1937 Royal Train livery (LNWR colours with LMS

markings). They are in full running order and are used from time to time as service vehicles for trains hauled by Museum locomotives.

North Eastern Railway Dynamometer Car (1906)

This is the coach that was used to record the maximum speed of 126 m.p.h. achieved by *Mallard* in July 1938. Until the construction of the stationary locomotive testing plants at Swindon and Rugby, the only accurate way of determining a locomotive's power output was by the use of a dynamometer car such as this. The drawbar, which is coupled to the engine's tender, has, at its opposite end, a large spring, the movement of which is calibrated so that the pull being exerted by the locomotive can be recorded. The moving paper roll on the recording Table is driven forward 2 ft for every mile travelled, and on it are traced graphs of the drawbar pull and the speed. By combining these two variables by means of a mechanical integrator, the horsepower is also recorded. The small labels in the vehicle, prepared by Mr Peter Howe of British Rail's Derby Technical Centre, fully describe all the recording equipment and how it works. Also in the vehicle is the equipment necessary for the staff who would, during test runs, spend the whole day on the job, well away from their normal base. Although originally built to a design by Wilson Worsdell, the vehicle has been considerably modified, and it is now carried on Gresley bogies and finished in LNER livery. The ninth wheel, used to record accurately the distance moved by the vehicle, can also be seen.

East Coast Joint Stock Passenger Brake Van No. 82 (LNER No. 109) (1908)

This coach is believed to be the oldest surviving vehicle designed by Nigel Gresley still in substantially original condition. It was built at Doncaster as East Coast Joint Stock No. 82 for use with the East Coast Royal Train, but it is externally in all essentials a standard Great Northern Railway vehicle, with the bow-ended, domed-roof configuration which was a trademark of the East Coast Route trains until after the Second World War. Renumbered as 109 by the LNER, the

55. *Six-wheel Midland Railway coach of 1885, restored by British Rail Engineering Ltd workshops at Wolverton.*

vehicle remained allocated to Royal Train use throughout its life, and after withdrawal in 1976, it was overhauled by British Rail Engineering Ltd at Doncaster in 1977.

East Coast Joint Stock Royal Saloon No. 395 (1908)
In 1908/9 the Great Northern and North Eastern Railways built a pair of Royal Saloons for use on the East Coast Route. Both were designed by Nigel Gresley, the Carriage & Wagon Superintendent of the GNR, and No. 395, the King's Saloon, was built at Doncaster by that railway, while the sister vehicle was constructed in York by the NER. In 1925 No. 395 was converted for day purposes only, and was exclusively used by Queen Mary, whose monograms are seen on some of the windows. In 1953, Queen Elizabeth the Queen Mother took the vehicle over, and it was refurbished to her requirements. Subsequently it was painted in royal claret over the original varnished teak livery. No. 395 did not need to undergo any restoration when it was handed over to the Museum in 1979. Its sister vehicle is on loan to the Bressingham Steam Museum.

Pullman Parlour Car 'Topaz' (1913)
This vehicle was built for the Pullman Car Company by the Birmingham Railway Carriage & Wagon Company at Smethwick in 1913. The Pullman Car was an American invention, and, even forty years after the first introduction of these vehicles in this country, they still retained many different features. Most important of these is the integral construction of body and underframe, all of which are built principally from wood. At least six different woods are used for the main construction, excluding the decorative inlaid marquetry panelling used in the interior.

Originally this vehicle operated on the South Eastern & Chatham Railway, but in the 1920s it was painted in the traditional British Pullman livery of umber and cream as exhibited. The main saloon is not furnished but one of the end coupés has been left in its 1960 condition, while the other has been restored to its 1913 form. The vehicle was presented to the Clapham Museum by the generosity of Mr Henry Maxwell and the Pullman Car Co. Ltd, then still a separate entity, but, since 1 January 1963, a wholly-owned subsidiary of British Railways.

Midland Railway Third-Class Dining Carriage (1914)
The Midland Railway was one of the best pre-1923 companies in Britain from the point of view of the comfort of its carriages. This particular vehicle displays many features typical of that company, including the characteristic Midland type of clerestory roof, first introduced at the turn of the century. Only part of the interior of the dining section has been fully restored, the remaining area having been used to house exhibition cases at Clapham, where the vehicle was exhibited in Midland & Glasgow & South Western Railway livery.

London & North Western Railway Broad Street Electric Motor Coach (1916)
After the LNWR had taken over the North London Railway in 1909, they electrified the busy suburban line from Broad Street to Richmond, using direct current at 630 volts, with a third- and fourth-rail supply system. The motor coaches were built by the Metropolitan Carriage, Wagon & Finance Company, and their electrical equipment was provided by Maschinenfabrik Oerlikon of Switzerland. This particular vehicle was originally No. 31E and remained at work until 1963, although in its latter years the unit was only used for shunting. LNW and LMS monograms can be seen in the glass of the passenger doors.

Southern Railway Motor Coach from Class 1285 Set No. 1293 (1925)
The Southern Railway carried out an extensive suburban electrification scheme in and around London from 1923 onwards, using the pioneering third-rail direct-current system of the London & South Western Railway, first introduced in 1915. This vehicle was built new for the Southern Railway, by the Metropolitan Carriage, Wagon & Finance Company, and thus differed from the original sets which were converted from steam-hauled stock. They were three-car units with motor coaches at each end of the close-coupled trailer. At peak

56. *King Edward VII's Saloon from the London & North Western Railway.*

periods two additional trailers were sandwiched between a pair of the three-car sets, but after the Second World War the operating arrangements were altered to give four-car sets, coded 4-SUB. Vehicle No. 8143 became part of Set No. 4308, which was withdrawn from passenger service in 1962, but was subsequently used as a de-icing unit.

London, Midland & Scottish Railway Third-Class Sleeping Car No. 14241 (1928)
This coach, typical of those constructed in the 1920s, is one of the first vehicles built to accommodate third-class sleeping passengers. This was achieved by means of fold-away bunks above the seats, which allow the coach to be used as an orthodox side-corridor vehicle by day, each compartment being convertible to a four-berth sleeping area at night.

The coach body is predominantly of wood construction, mounted on a substantial steel chassis. It was built at Derby and completely restored by British Rail Engineering Ltd, Wolverton, most of the fittings being original. Three compartments have been re-trimmed in 1920s-pattern upholstery (specially re-woven for the purpose), while the other four retain the BR trim carried at the time of withdrawal. The vehicle is in full running order.

LNER Third-Class Sleeper Section and Articulated Bogie (1931)
In 1928 sleeping cars were first introduced in this country for third-class passengers. For the previous fifty or so years only first-class passengers were provided with such accommodation, and the new vehicles were laid out with four-berth compartments as shown in this exhibit, which was a section taken from one of Gresley's later twin articulated units built in 1931. The bunks in this particular class were not convertible to day use.

These twin units were mounted on three bogies, the central one carrying the inner ends of the two vehicles. The bogie unit concerned is also on display elsewhere in the Museum to enable visitors to see the arrangement of the suspension and articulation.

Great Western Railway Diesel Railcar No. 4 (1934)
During the 1930s the Great Western, in conjunction with AEC, pioneered the use of diesel railcars, using engines of the type installed extensively in buses, and having mechanical transmissions, comprising Wilson epicyclic gearboxes and fluid flywheels. Railcar No. 4 was built for the Birmingham–Cardiff service, and provided forty-four seats with a buffet counter for passengers. It had two 121 h.p. engines, and a maximum speed of 80 m.p.h. The vehicle was withdrawn for preservation in 1958 and has been extensively restored for static exhibition at York.

Wagons-Lits Sleeping Car No. 3792 (1936)
This coach, built for the Wagons-Lits Company in France, was one of the first of the only series of passenger vehicles designed to operate both in Britain and Europe. Until the early 1970s, it ran regularly on the London–Paris and London–Brussels 'Night Ferry' services from Victoria Station, which were withdrawn in October 1980. The cross-Channel part of the journey was made by specially-equipped train-ferry ships operating between Dover and Dunkirk.

The coach is very much in the Continental idiom, but built to smaller overall dimensions to enable it to run in Britain where clearances are more restricted. Inside are nine twin-berth compartments which can be arranged in a variety of configurations for either day or night travel. Heating was by means of a solid fuel stove, thus allowing the coach to be kept warm, even when not part of a train. It was restored to its original condition and full running order at the Ostend works of the Wagons-Lits Company, whose famous blue and gold colour scheme it carries.

LMS Dynamometer Car and Mobile Testing Unit (1936)
In order to measure and improve the performance capabilities of their locomotives, the LMS ordered a special test train in 1936, but it was not completed until after the Second World War. The Museum possesses the dynamometer car and one of the three mobile braking units, each of which could be used to absorb up to 1,500 h.p. (1,120 kW) and so simulate the effect of quite a lengthy train. The Museum has repainted the dynamometer car in the LMS livery it would have carried had it been completed before nationalisation.

Southern Railway Electric Motor Coach No. 11179 (1937)
The Southern Railway introduced electric working from Waterloo to Portsmouth Harbour in 1937. This was the longest of their routes so far electrified, and a new design of four-car multiple unit was provided. Some of them contained restaurant cars and, in order to give access to these from the whole of the train, vestibule connections were installed at the driving ends of the power cars which were marshalled at each end of the units. When the vestibules were in use, the door cleverly shut off the motorman's compartment. This vehicle, from Set No. 3131, was built at Eastleigh and ran until 1972. Externally, it has been repainted in its original Southern Railway livery.

London & North Eastern Railway Buffet Car No. 9135 (1937)
This vehicle is an example of the once familiar teak-bodied, bow-ended coaches designed by Nigel Gresley, and was the last such coach to run as a passenger-carrying vehicle, not being withdrawn until 1977. The robust construction of these coaches encouraged BR to redesign the interior completely in the 1950s, with modern furnishings and catering equipment. The vehicle was refurbished in the Museum for use on the railway catering 'Centenary Express' in 1979. Externally it is in its original LNER varnished teak livery, and the interior of the passenger compartment has been restored as closely as possible to the 1930s style.

LMS Royal Saloons Nos. 798/799 (1941)
Although these new vehicles for King George VI and Queen Elizabeth were ordered in 1938, they were not completed until the war was already in progress, and consequently, until the end of hostilities, they were fitted with armour plating to protect their occupants during their morale-boosting tours of the country. Their interiors are much simpler in style than the 1902 LNWR vehicles which they replaced. In 1954 their livery was changed to 'royal claret'. After they had been handed over to the Museum in 1978, although the Queen's Saloon (No. 799) was repainted in the same colours, the King's Saloon, which had been used by the Duke of Edinburgh, reverted to the immediate post-war LMS livery. The latter vehicle was used to convey the Duke to York for the opening of the Museum in September 1975.

British Railways Open Coach No. E4286 (1956)
This vehicle is a standard British Railways' Mark I coach built in 1956. Its classification was TSO, or Tourist Second Open, and it had sixty-four seats. It was acquired by the National Railway Museum to accommodate visiting school parties, who use it as a children's lunchroom as well as for project work. Applications for its use should be made to the Booking Section. It is now painted externally in the first BR standard livery of crimson and cream, used until 1956.

Pullman Cars 'Emerald' and 'Eagle' (1960)
In the period after the Second World War, there were a number of important Pullman Car expresses on the East Coast Route, and a batch of new, all-steel, cars was built for these services by the Metropolitan Carriage & Wagon Co. in 1960. They combined the early BR standard body profile with the traditional Pullman vestibules and recessed end doors. Pullman cars continued running on the East Coast Route until 1978, when they were superseded by the first of the 'Inter-City 125' units. *Eagle* includes a kitchen, so the pair of vehicles can still be used to prepare and serve meals on special occasions. They operate on steam specials over BR from time-to-time, in conjunction with a rake of similar vehicles owned by the Steam Locomotive Operators' Association. The NRM vehicles were restored externally to their original livery by British Rail Engineering Ltd at Wolverton in 1979, but retain the later form of seating which replaced the original individual armchairs.

British Railways Mark I Griddle Car No. Sc. 1100 (1960)
This vehicle represents the first phase (1951–63) of standard coach building by the nationalised British Railways. Of all-steel construction, it also illustrates one of several alternatives to the traditional orthodox dining car which were introduced by BR during this period. A small dining saloon is capable of serving buffet-style snacks as well as grilled meals, which often featured prime Angus steaks. There is also a saloon bar, and the two passenger areas are separated by a central servery/kitchen/bar counter. The vehicle was the prototype of its class, and spent most of its working life in Scotland. It is carried on

57. *The 'Night Ferry' Wagons-Lits sleeping car.*

58. *Replica 'Dandy-Cart' of 1828.*

Commonwealth pattern bogies and is capable of 100 m.p.h. running if need be. It is in the BR maroon livery of the 1956–64 period.

British Railways Experimental Advanced Passenger Train (1972)

This unit, known as the APT-E, completed its test programme in April 1976, and was presented to the Museum by British Railways. Of lightweight construction, it is powered by ten gas-turbine engines with electrical transmission. Special bogies are used which permit curves to be traversed at high speeds. The vehicles can be tilted when running to maintain existing standards of comfort at higher speeds on curved tracks. Hydrokinetic brakes are contained in the large-diameter axles, and enable the unit to be brought to a stand from high speeds within the same distance as a conventional train. In 1975, while on a test between Didcot and Swindon, this train set up a British Rail speed record of 152 m.p.h. (245 km/h.). Since its arrival at York one of the cars has been split out of the unit, and has been arranged so that it can display the way in which the vehicle tilts on curves. British Railways have built three prototype electrically-powered versions of the train, which made their first public passenger journey between Glasgow and Euston in December 1981.

FREIGHT AND SERVICE VEHICLES

Peak Forest Canal Co. Truck (1797)

This is believed to be the oldest vehicle preserved in Britain that runs on a track. The Company was authorised by Act of Parliament in 1794 to construct a tramroad from its Peak Forest limestone quarries to the termination of the canal at Bugsworth (now Buxworth). It was built by Benjamin Outram to a gauge of 4 ft 2 in., a standard at that time, and opened in 1796. The rails were of the plate type, 3 ft long and laid on stone blocks, this form of trackwork being used extensively for tramroad construction. The line became part of the Manchester, Sheffield & Lincolnshire Railway (later Great Central Railway) in 1883 and did not close until 1922, when it was still a tramroad. The trucks were of iron and were used to transport limestone to the canal, the end door enabling their contents to

be tipped into barges. They were horsedrawn in 'gangs' and braking was achieved using 'sprags': a stout iron bar put through the wheel spokes so that the wheel jammed.

Belvoir Castle Railway Wagon (1815)

This is the oldest vehicle with flanged wheels that is preserved in Britain. It was one of those used on the private railway constructed for the Duke of Rutland to enable coal and other freight to be carried from the Grantham Canal to his castle. The railway was an early example of edge-rail construction, and the vehicle is shown on track of this type, set on stone blocks in what amounts to the equivalent of a rough country lane.

Chaldron Wagons (1826 onwards)

The Museum has several chaldron wagons, the oldest of them, from Cramlington Colliery, Northumberland, dating from 1826. These vehicles were a familiar sight long before the days of steam, and they were used to carry coal on the wagonways in the North-East for many years. They were designed to hold a 'Newcastle Chaldron' of coal which was 2 tons 13 cwt (2·69 tonnes), and was the standard quantity in which large-scale deliveries of coal were made in the North-East.

The two most recent chaldron wagons are from the South Hetton and Londonderry private railway systems in Co. Durham. These vehicles remained in use until the 1950s. One of them is mounted on the Gaunless Bridge, and the other is in the South-East garden.

The 'Dandy-Cart' replica (1828)

The Stockton & Darlington Railway was laid out by Stephenson so that the gradients were favourable for loaded wagons on their eastbound journey from the collieries to Darlington and Stockton. For much of the distance the vehicles would run under the action of gravity alone. In the summer of 1828 Thomas Brandreth had proposed the adoption of a special cart – the 'Dandy-Cart' – on the rear of the train where the horse could ride over the downhill sections. The original suggestion for this method of transport had, however, been made by George Stephenson some two years earlier for the Canterbury & Whitstable Railway but it had not been adopted. After these vehicles had been introduced, the weekly mileage obtained from a horse went up from 174 to 240, an increase of practically forty per cent. The origins of the vehicle in the Museum are uncertain, but it was either constructed as a replica, or restored at the Shildon Works of the North Eastern Railway, probably about seventy years ago.

Shell Mex and National Benzole Tank Wagons (1889 and 1954)

These two vehicles are examples of special-purpose wagons privately owned and registered to run on the main-line

59. *Tank wagons from the Museum's freight vehicle collection.*

railways in this country. The Shell Mex wagon (No. 512) was built as long ago as 1889, while the National Benzole one (No. 2022) was constructed in 1954. Both were reconditioned by their owners, and presented to the National Collection. They provide interesting contrasts showing the changes in design that took place during a period of seventy-five years. Even greater changes have taken place since 1954 with rail tank wagons, many of which now have gross weights of 100 tons, and operate at high speeds behind diesel and electric locomotives.

Great Western Railway Shunter's Truck No. W94988 (1914)
The GWR used to keep a special truck coupled to most of its shunting locomotives. This provided storage space for equipment such as the shunting poles and brake-sticks, and also gave the shunter a convenient and relatively safe place on which to ride during the engine's longer movements up and down the yards.

ICI Nitric Acid Tank Wagon (1928)
The chemical industry transports large quantities of its products by rail. This tank wagon was used for the movement of nitric acid which is widely used in the manufacture of dyestuffs, fertilisers and explosives. It was based at Billingham and operated to all parts of the country. The barrel is made of stainless steel to withstand the corrosive nature of the acid and the livery is typical of that used on ICI vehicles up to the 1960s.

Paris–Lyon Mediterranée Ferry Van No. 475014 (1935)
This van was one of 400 identical vehicles owned by the PLM Railway in France, and was built to convey perishable loads from France to England using the train-ferry services instituted in 1936. The vehicle was presented to the National Railway Museum by the French Railways, and a second, identical, van has been restored for exhibition at the French Railway Museum in Mulhouse. Both are planned to be used to display similar exhibitions depicting the history of the Anglo-French railway shipping services.

London Midland & Scottish Railway 12-ton Dropside Wagon No. 472867 (1936)
The open freight wagon in its various forms has been the most common vehicle to be used on the railways of this country. This particular one is of the 'three-plank' type, and the whole of each side drops down for loading and unloading. It has been restored to LMS livery by British Railways at St Blazey.

Ministry of Supply 16-ton Open Wagon No. ADB192437 (1946)
After the Liberation of France at the end of the Second World War, the Ministry of Supply built 7,000 wagons specially for the French Railways. The design was essentially a French-style body on a British underframe, and each vehicle was sent to France as components in 'knocked-down' form. All but a few of them were later returned to England and reconditioned to run on British Railways. It is proposed to restore the vehicle to the form in which it ran on the French Railways as SNCF No. T7738227.

British Railways Cattle Wagons Nos. B892156 and B893343 (1950 and 1951)
Before the coming of the railways, cattle were driven to large towns 'on the hoof', quite often travelling long distances along the ancient Drove Roads. For over a century they travelled by rail, but since 1976 all cattle transport has been by road, although it is now common for the animals to be slaughtered near the farm and then transported in the form of meat. These two vehicles were the last in use on British Railways.

British Railways Special Cattle Van No. S3733S (1951)
Cattle being transported by the railways could in effect travel first- or second-class. In addition to the two partially-open cattle wagons mentioned above, Special Cattle Vans were provided for moving pedigree cattle to shows and so on. This is one such vehicle, built at Lancing, and has a compartment for the drover between the two spaces for the animals.

ICI Chlorine Tank Wagon (1951)
Chlorine is used extensively in industry and is usually transported in liquefied form under pressure. This particular vehicle was one of a batch of fifty and was presented to the Museum by ICI Mond Division. The barrel has a working pressure of 174 lb per sq. in. (12 bar). It contains a 'dip' pipe running from the dome to the bottom of the barrel, which enables the chlorine to be discharged as a liquid under pressure. The basic barrel livery is that used for all wagons containing liquids under pressure.

British Railways Iron Ore Tippler Wagon (1954)
Until the Second World War, most of the coal and mineral traffic on our railways had been carried in privately-owned wagons, which were commandeered during the hostilities. To cope with the vastly increased tonnages of freight being carried, the Ministry of War Transport introduced standard all-steel mineral wagons, and this vehicle represents a variant of the original design. Because it was discharged by being inverted in a 'tippler', no doors were needed on this particular wagon, in contrast to the more normal version which had two side- and one end-door.

British Railways Horsebox No. S96369 (1957)
Until recent years the railways transported large numbers of horses, many of them to and from race meetings. Special vehicles were used, capable of being attached to express trains. This is one of those built by British Railways at Earlestown for use on the Southern Region. In the centre there are stalls for up to three horses with a grooms' compartment and lavatory. At each end there is storage space for fodder, one of them being accessible during the journey.

British Railways Banana Van (1960)
The transport of bananas from the docks to the distribution warehouses used to provide considerable traffic for the railways. The arrival of a banana boat at places such as Avonmouth, Garston or Barry would often result in the running of a number of special fitted-freight trains to distribute the fruit around the country. Insulated vans were used to ensure that the bunches were not exposed to extremes of temperature during their journey, some also being steam-heated to ripen the fruit.

Other Wagons

Amongst the other wagons likely to be on exhibition in the Museum from time to time are the following:

London & South Western Brake Van No. 99 (1894)
London & South Western Railway Open Carriage Truck No. 5830 (1895)
North Eastern Railway 20-ton Hopper Wagon No. 4551 (1902)
London Brighton & South Coast Railway Open Wagon No. 3537 (1912)
Great Eastern Railway Sand Wagon No. DE14974
Great Northern Railway 8-ton Van No. 432764
Great Western Railway 'Lowmac' No. 42193 (1919)
Great Western Railway Van No. 042431 (1931)
Stanton Iron Works 12-ton Mineral Wagon
London & North Eastern Railway 20-ton Goods Brake Van No. 187774 (1936)
London Midland & Scottish Railway Tube Wagon No. 499254 (1936)
London Midland & Scottish Railway Single Bolster Wagon No. 722702 (1938)
London Midland & Scottish Railway 'Lowmac' No. 700728 (1944)
London & North Eastern Railway 20-ton Hopper Wagon No. 270919 (1946)
British Railways 40-ton 'Weltrol' No. DB900402 (1949)
British Railways Iron Ore Hopper No. B436275 (1950)
British Railways 40-ton 'Weltrol MC' No. B900805 (1950)
British Railways 30-ton Bogie Bolster Wagon No. B943139 (1952)
British Railways 'Conflat' No. B737725 (1959)
War Department 'Warflat' No. 161042 (1940)

60. *A chaldron wagon on the Stockton & Darlington Railway Gaunless Bridge beside the Museum car park.*

Other Exhibits

Other Exhibits

Gaunless Bridge (1825)
This bridge spanned the River Gaunless on the original route of the Stockton & Darlington Railway, west of Shildon. Three spans were erected in 1823 by John and Isaac Burrell of Orchard Street, Newcastle upon Tyne, to the design of George Stephenson. The fourth span was erected in 1825 following damage by flooding, and the bridge was brought into use when the line was opened on 27 September 1825. The branch used horse traction until 1856 when it fell into disuse. The bridge remained intact until the 1900s when it was dismantled. It was later re-erected in the Queen Street Museum at York for its opening in 1927. Now it has been assembled on a site alongside the car park, with a chaldron wagon mounted on it.

North Eastern Railway Water Column (1920)
This water column, situated between the tracks at the north end of the Museum, was constructed in 1920 and still stands in its original position where it provided many thousands of gallons of water for the locomotives leaving the former engine shed. The water was pumped from the River Ouse.

Bristol & Exeter Railway locomotive wheels (1877)
These wheels were used on a locomotive of the Bristol & Exeter Railway and had a diameter of 8 ft 10 in. (270 cm). They are believed to be the largest locomotive wheels in existence and were used on the broad gauge of 7 ft 0¼ in (214 cm). The wheels are flangeless to help the locomotive negotiate sharp curves, like the centre driving wheels on *Evening Star*. Further research is needed to determine the reason for only two eccentrics on the driving axle.

Great Northern Signal
The highest of the three arms on this post was the Up 'Home' or stop signal controlling admission to Peterborough Station from the North. Next below it is the 'Distant' giving advance information about the position of the signals at the next box to the South. This arm is painted red as it was in 1925, before yellow was adopted for distant signals. The smaller arm at the bottom is to permit a second train to follow slowly after one that is departing from the platform. A bracket post was used at this point to place the signals over the track for better visibility. The Great Northern Railway adopted centrally-pivoted somersault arms following the Abbots Ripton accident of 1876 when signals froze in the all-clear position.

Weatherhill Winding Engine (1833)
When the Stanhope & Tyne Railway was opened in 1833, wagons were hauled out of Weardale up two rope-worked inclines, to a height of more than 1400 ft (425 m) above sea level. The lower of these was known as the Crawley Incline and the other was the Weatherhill, which was just over a mile in length with gradients as steep as 1 in 12. The winding engine here was of 50 nominal horsepower (37 kW), and consisted of a single vertical cylinder 2 ft 4 in (71 cm) diameter by 5 ft (152 cm) stroke. The piston cross-head is supported by parallel-motion arms from the side walls. The two winding drums were each 9 ft (2·7 m) in diameter, gear-driven from the main flywheel shaft. This massive engine was replaced in 1919 by a much smaller marine-type installation. However, a few years later the new engine broke down, and the old machine was brought back into use temporarily. Subsequently the main items of the original machinery were reassembled in the Queen Street Museum at York. With the greater space available in this Museum, the engine has been restored to a working condition, complete with a new flywheel, being driven by electric power. The engine is normally demonstrated twice daily.

The Swannington Incline Winding Engine (1833)
The Leicester & Swannington Railway was built to bring coal to Leicester and was completed in 1833. At its north-western end there was an incline half a mile long with a gradient of 1 in 17. A stationary engine was constructed to haul wagons up this incline by means of a cable on a drum, driven from the engine by

means of gears. The engine has a single horizontal cylinder, and to ensure that this was not worn oval by the weight of the piston, a tail rod and slippers were provided to support the weight of the piston on its shaft. Another interesting feature is the use of a piston valve on the cylinder at a very early date. When the engine ceased working in 1947 it was removed to the old York Railway Museum. It has now been completely restored with a new flywheel, and can be made to rotate by an electric motor being normally demonstrated twice daily. Photographs on the wall behind show the original installation.

Sulzer Diesel Engine and British Thomson-Houston Generators (1960)
This is the diesel engine and its associated generators from one of the Class 24 diesel-electric locomotives. The motor with its six cylinders developed 1160 h.p. (865 kW) and was directly coupled to the generators, which produced the direct-current electrical supply for the motors mounted on the bogies. Above the generator is the pressure charger, driven by the exhaust gases. Some of the interior construction of the engine has been made visible for exhibition purposes. The blue pipes carried cooling water, the pink ones lubricating oil, and the brown ones diesel fuel. Electrical wiring was enclosed in the orange conduits.

Electric Locomotive Traction Motor
This 775 h.p. (578 kW) motor is from a Class 84 electric locomotive, an example of which is on loan to the Museum and described in the Locomotives section of this Guide. The armature has been taken out of the case so that the various components can be studied. Visitors can see such items as the field coils, inter-poles, brush gear and the commutator.

Diesel-electric locomotive bogie (1958)
This bogie is one of those used on the Class 24 Bo-Bo diesel-electric locomotives, built from 1958 onwards. The two direct-current electric motors can be seen, with their leads, each driving one of the axles. One of the casings has been removed to show the reduction gears. The circular bellows on top of the motors convey cooling air from the blowers in the body of the locomotive. Compressed air for the four brake cylinders (one of which is sectioned) on the frames is carried through the white piping. In addition to the springs on each axle, the body of the locomotive is supported by means of the sprung beam across the centre of the bogie, which also permits it to move relative to the body around curves and over irregularities in the track.

61. *The restored Weatherhill winding engine.*

62. *Diesel engine and generator.*

British Railways Standard Coach Sections (1951)

These two full-scale mock-ups represent the first design of British Railways' compartment coaches for first- and third-class passengers. At that time, except for certain boat trains, there was no second-class stock in use on British Railways, but in 1956 the third-class vehicles were all re-classified as second-class in conformity with standard European practice.

Replica of cab of British Railways Locomotive No. 71000 'Duke of Gloucester' (1954)

This cab section was built as a mock-up for the construction of the sole example of the largest British Railways' design of steam locomotive, *Duke of Gloucester*. The driver's position is on the left, with most of his controls situated within easy reach. The fireman had a seat on the right which he was able to use for those short periods when he was not having to stoke the fire.

7¼ in.-Gauge Locomotives

The Museum possesses two 7¼ in.-gauge (20 cm) working model locomotives, based on very different prototypes which both ran on 2 ft-gauge (60 cm) lines. One is a commercially-built model of the 1897 Manning Wardle 2–4–2T *Taw*, which worked on the Lynton & Barnstaple Railway until its closure in 1935. The other, *Margaret*, was built in the Museum workshops, and represents one of the Hunslet 0–4–0STs which operated in the slate quarries of North Wales. It hauled the Prince of Wales during his visit to the Museum in November 1981.

Cornwall Railway Coach Section (c. 1860)

This section represents a third of a length of a Cornwall Railway coach which was found in use as a hut on the lineside in Cornwall, and rescued by the Museum in 1977. Since then it has been rebuilt by Museum staff, and visitors can gain some idea of the conditions under which third-class passengers travelled in the latter half of the nineteenth century. The hut appears to have been in use on the lineside since 1892, when the Broad Gauge was converted.

Horse-Drawn Vehicles

The privately-owned railways of Britain were considerable users of horse-drawn vehicles, and the Museum collection of items includes several interesting examples from this bygone period. Those likely to be on display during the currency of this guide comprise:

Kent & East Sussex Railway Horse Bus

This vehicle was built by W. J. Mercer Carriage Works in Tenterden. It was acquired by the Kent & East Sussex Railway in 1916. Initially it was used between Rolvenden station and Tenterden itself, but after the line had been extended it remained in use until 1923, working from Tenterden Town Station. Amongst the more notable passengers known to have

been carried by this vehicle were Dame Ellen Terry and the Right Honourable Arthur Balfour.

Midland Railway Heavy Duty Dray

A massively-built vehicle used for the conveyance of heavy loads, with the carrying platform set very low between the rear wheels.

London & South Western Railway Horse Ambulance

This vehicle was used for recovering 'fallen' horses from the streets, the canvas web between the sides of the vehicle being used to support the belly of the injured animal.

Lancashire & Yorkshire Railway Delivery Van

A very common type of horse vehicle, for the delivery of parcels and small consignments in the district served by a station.

Clock from the Great Hall of Euston Station (1837)

This clock stood in the Great Hall at Euston from 1849 until it was demolished in 1963. It is believed to have been first used on the station platforms from 1837. It is 15 ft 9 in (4·8 m) high, and its dial 4 ft (1·2 m) in diameter. It requires winding by hand twice a week.

Gravesend Station Clock

Although latterly situated at Barking, this clock was originally installed on Gravesend Pier Station, which recalls the Thames ferries operated by the London, Tilbury & Southend Railway. This company's operations ultimately became part of the Eastern Region of British Railways, which explains the BR(E) to be seen faintly on some of the faces.

London & North Western Railway quarter-scale coach models

These two models were built at Wolverton Works, and depict King Edward VII's Saloon as first built in 1903, and a composite dining saloon of 1910. All the details of the interiors of the full-scale vehicles are very well portrayed. Both were at one time exhibited in the Great Hall at Euston, and the model of the Royal Saloon won a gold medal in the 1904 St Louis Exposition.

Signalling Exhibit

This exhibit has been constructed in the Museum to show visitors the operation of two typical pairs of points. The first is

63. *Lancashire & Yorkshire Railway delivery van.*

worked mechanically from a small lever frame and includes all the necessary interlocking, detection, and so on. At the opposite end there is a similar installation, this time worked by electricity, constructed from part of the electro-mechanical frame that was originally installed at Holborn Viaduct. Demonstrations of the operation of the points and signalling are given from time to time. Nearby is a Midland Railway signal that was in use at Uffington & Barnack until 1974.

Station Seats
The Museum has an extensive collection of station seats, many of them very decorative. The owning company's initials are often included in the cast-iron ends, while those from the Furness Railway have squirrels eating bunches of grapes. Many of the seats carry the name of their station. Most are fairly easily recognisable, but the one marked 'Grimsby C B' was used at the **C**orporation **B**ridge terminus of the Grimsby & Immingham Electric Railway, a railway-operated tramway, built in connection with the new railway docks at Immingham in 1912.

Blenkinsop Locomotive Wheels (c. 1812)
These wheels are of the type used by John Blenkinsop on the Middleton Railway near Leeds which was opened in 1812 at a time when it was considered that there was not sufficient

friction between iron wheels and rails to permit effective steam traction. William Hedley on Tyneside showed that smooth wheels were technically feasible, and no more rack railways were built after 1812 until late in the nineteenth century when the now-familiar mountain railways were first developed. These wheels and the associated track were originally at the Newburn Steel Works and were presented by them to the old York Railway Museum.

Atmospheric Railway Tube (c. 1848)
The idea of an atmospheric railway was that trains were drawn along by a piston running in a tube set between the rails. Stationary engines exhausted some of the air in the tube ahead of the trains, and the atmospheric pressure entering behind the piston drove it, and the train, along. The system was used on short railways at Croydon and at Dalkey in Ireland. It was then adopted by Brunel for the South Devon Railway, but quickly proved a failure, the continuous leather seal along the top proving impossible to maintain satisfactorily. This section of tube was cast by the well-known Coalbrookdale Company for the Croydon scheme, but the Museum also possesses a section of the South Devon tube.

Euston Turntable
When the earliest terminal stations, such as the one at Euston, were opened, they were provided with only two platforms. Between them there would be sidings, and the four-wheeled passenger coaches would be moved from one to the other by means of short cross lengths of track and small turntables. This turntable came from the original Euston Station, the layout of which is shown in the Diorama on the Balcony, and was unearthed during excavations for the present station.

Wagon Turntable
This small turntable was one of those installed by the Leeds & Selby Railway for turning wagons in goods yards.

London & North Western Railway Water Column
This water column was in use at Coventry station from 1847 until 1962, and shows the ornamentation provided on such relatively utilitarian railway installations in the early days.

Italian Memorial to George Stephenson
This memorial to George Stephenson was presented to the railwaymen of Britain by the Italian State Railway in 1925 on the occasion of the Centenary of the Stockton & Darlington Railway. At the bottom are representations of *Locomotion* and the then latest Italian 2–8–2 passenger locomotives. The 'flying wheel' *motif* is the symbol of the Italian State Railways.

England/Scotland Border Sign
This sign marked the crossing of the English/Scottish border near Deadwater in Northumberland, on the now-closed line from Hexham to Riccarton Junction.

Great Western Railway Signal
This signal carries both a distant arm (yellow with slotted end) and a stop arm (red with a squared end). The Great Western normally used lower-quadrant signals, which fell from the horizontal into the 'off' position. This particular example is unusual in that it was converted to upper-quadrant operation and was installed just north of Oxford after Nationalisation.

Newcastle & Carlisle Railway Drinking Fountain (1860)
In the days before the use of motor transport, the railways often provided drinking facilities for the use of horses at stations. This very ornamental trough came from Blaydon. On the other side of the garden is an 1875 drinking trough of the type frequently installed on the platforms for the convenience of passengers.

London & North Eastern Railway Signal Box
In certain circumstances signal lever frames were installed at ground level where it was not necessary for the signalman to operate from an elevated position. This is a typical example of such a small LNER box of the 1930s

64. *The clock from the Great Hall at Euston.*